MENTAL HEALTH IN A CHANGING COMMUNITY

MENTAL HEALTH IN
A CHANGING COMMUNITY

BASED ON A SYMPOSIUM JOINTLY SPONSORED BY THE
SAN FRANCISCO ASSOCIATION FOR MENTAL HEALTH AND THE
DEPARTMENT OF CONTINUING EDUCATION IN MEDICINE
AND THE HEALTH SCIENCES,
UNIVERSITY OF CALIFORNIA MEDICAL CENTER

Edited by

Reed Brockbank, M.D.
Dorothy Westby-Gibson, Ed.D.

GRUNE & STRATTON
NEW YORK AND LONDON

Library of Congress Card Catalog No. 66-22942

Printed in U.S.A. (K-A)

CONTRIBUTORS

Alfred Auerback, M.D.: Associate Clinical Professor of Psychiatry, University of California School of Medicine, San Francisco, Calif.

Richard A. Bancroft, L.L.D., L.L.M.: Attorney-at-law, San Francisco, Calif.

Klaus W. Berblinger, M.D.: Professor of Psychiatry, University of California School of Medicine, San Francisco, Calif.

Walcott H. Beatty, Ph.D.: Professor of Psychology, San Francisco State College, San Francisco, Calif.

Egon Bittner, Ph.D.: Research Social Scientist, Langley Porter Neuropsychiatric Institute; Lecturer in Psychiatry, University of California School of Medicine, San Francisco, Calif.

Reed Brockbank, M.D.: Assistant Clinical Professor, Department of Psychiatry, University of California School of Medicine, San Francisco; Psychiatric Consultant, Community Mental Health Training Program, Langley Porter Neuropsychiatric Institute, San Francisco, Calif.

John A. Clausen, Ph.D.: Professor of Sociology and Director, Institute of Human Development, University of California, Berkeley, Calif.

Kenneth Mark Colby, M.D.: Research Associate, Computer Science, Stanford University, Palo Alto, Calif.

Peter Cohen, M.D.: Associate Professor of Pediatrics, University of California School of Medicine, San Francisco, Calif.

John B. Condliffe, D.Sc.: Director, Basic Economic Research, Stanford Research Institute, Menlo Park, Calif.

William R. Dennes, D.Phil.: Mills Professor of Intellectual and Moral Philosophy and Civil Policy, University of California, Berkeley, Calif.

Sir John C. Eccles, M.D., F.R.S.: Professor of Physiology, The John Curtain School of Medical Research, Canberra, Australia. Nobel Laureate in Medicine.

Harry B. Friedgood, M.D., F.A.C.P.: Associate Clinical Professor of Medicine and Associate Research Physician, George W. Hooper Foundation, University of California School of Medicine, San Francisco, Calif.

Ralph W. Gerard, M.D.: Director of Special Studies and Biological Sciences, University of California, Irvine, Calif.

Nathan Glazer, Ph.D.: Professor of Sociology and Chairman, Department of Social Studies Integrated Course, University of California, Berkeley, Calif.

M. Robert Harris, M.D.: Assistant Clinical Professor of Psychiatry, University of California School of Medicine, San Francisco; Director of Clinical Services, Langley Porter Neuropsychiatric Institute, San Francisco, Calif.

Ralph Lane, Jr., Ph.D.: Chairman, Department of Sociology, University of San Francisco, Calif.

Chauncey D. Leake, Ph.D.: Senior Lecturer in Pharmacology and in the History of Medicine; Coordinator, Medical Student Research Training Program, University of California Medical Center, San Francisco, Calif.

Robert C. Leslie, Ph.D.: Professor of Pastoral Psychology and Counseling, Pacific School of Religion, Berkeley, Calif.

Lawrence N. Loban: Training Supervisor, Crown Zellerbach Corporation, San Francisco; Chairman, Governor's Committee for Employment of the Handicapped.

Marjorie Fiske Lowenthal: Lecturer in Psychiatry, University of California School of Medicine, San Francisco, Calif.

James V. Lowry, M.D.: Director, State Department of Mental Hygiene, Sacramento, Calif.

Henry S. Maas, Ph.D.: Professor, School of Social Welfare, University of California, Berkeley, Calif.

Theresa S. Mahler: Director, Child Care Centers Division, San Francisco Unified School District, San Francisco, Calif.

Mrs. Winthrop Rockefeller: President, National Association for Mental Health, New York.

Malcolm S. M. Watts, M.D.: Assistant Dean and Associate Clinical Professor of Medicine, Board Trustee, Langley Porter Neuropsychiatric Institute.

Paul Watzlawick, Ph.D.: Research Associate, Mental Research Institute, Palo Alto, Calif.

Dorothy Westby-Gibson, Ed.D.: Professor of Education and Psychology, San Francisco State College, San Francisco; Chairman, Education Committee, San Francisco Association for Mental Health, San Francisco, Calif.

CONTENTS

DEVELOPMENTAL APPROACHES TO MENTAL HEALTH (THE SEARCH FOR A SOLUTION)

PEOPLE AS INDIVIDUALS: THEIR BIOLOGICAL AND SOCIAL LIMITS AND POSSIBILITIES—A COLLOQUIUM

PREFACE

Mental health, despite its conceptual ambiguity, is seen as a positive value and a goal toward which individuals and groups in the community are devoting an ever-increasing amount of effort, money, and attention. The assessment of community mental health would be immensely difficult if our social system were stable and unchanging, but the effect of constant social change on individuals and on groups enormously multiplies the complexity of any assessment of our present status, to say nothing of our plans for the future. Recent studies (i.e., the Manhattan Study, the Baltimore Study, and the New Haven Study) have increased the average person's awareness that we are not a mentally healthy society. At least, we have an abundance of mental and emotional discomfort and dysfunction, and we are far from achieving that hoped-for state of emotional well-being that we call mental health. In any case, attempts to look at the causes of our discomfort, or state of ill health, and to consider possible remedies must, of necessity, entail a multidisciplined approach in which all aspects of our society unite in a common cause. It was with such a view in mind that the San Francisco Association for Mental Health joined with the University of California, San Francisco Medical Center, Department of Continuing Education in Medicine and the Health Sciences, to sponsor a symposium which included a wide range of experts in the community who could contribute to the elucidation of the problem. The material presented in this symposium makes up the contents of this book. As in any such symposium, some portions are formal and explicit while others are discursive and informal. We have tried to combine both the formal presentations and the informal panel discussions so that they would form a cohesive whole and present a picture of the thinking of the participants.

INTRODUCTION

By MALCOLM S. W. WATTS, M.D.

I should like to try briefly to relate "Mental Health in a Changing Community" to a broader concept of health in our evolving society. The World Health Organization has defined health as "a state of complete physical, mental, and social well-being," and not merely the absence of disease. This definition, which is now being widely accepted as a working definition of health, implies a healthy relationship between the human individual and his environment. As physicians in a medical center, we are primarily concerned with man, the human being, but we cannot ignore the environment. The Chancellor of the San Francisco Medical Center, Dr. Saunders, has often expressed the fact, known to be true in biology and medicine, that each man, each individual, is unique. He is unlike any other individual. This fact is borne out simply by just looking at people. Even identical twins have some differences. Individual differences are particularly evident to those interested in psychiatry and to physicians as they delve further into the organic makeup of individuals, into the cell structure, and even into the molecular structure. It is quite evident that there are no two individuals who are alike.

But in society or the environment, the dominant social and political theory of the times is based on the assumption that men are not very different. It is held that all men are created equal and their inherent individuality is de-emphasized. This cultural blindness to biological fact has led to all sorts of unrealities. In time, the biological fact of human individuality will ultimately have to be recognized by society as well as by Medicine and Psychiatry, but for some time to come the ideal community, the environment in which everyone will live in a state of complete physical, mental, and social well-being, will be difficult to achieve. In the meantime, we can try to approach this most desirable goal by education and hard work. I am sure that these two threads, the uniqueness of the individual and the effort to make fact of the theoretical assumption that humans are all equal to one another, will be found weaving themselves through the following discussions. In many aspects of mental health in a changing community we must be concerned with these realities in modern society.

1

By Mrs. Winthrop Rockefeller

I am pleased to have the privilege of welcoming you to this symposium on "Mental Health in a Changing Community." My greetings and best wishes are extended to you on behalf of the National Association for Mental Health and the San Francisco Association for Mental Health.

I would like to compliment the wise choice of theme for this symposium: "Mental Health in a Changing Community," because it indicates an awareness that our American communities *are* changing.

What do we mean by changing? We are heartened to see that the approach to treatment of the mentally ill and the emotionally disturbed is now directed toward providing prompt assistance to the patient within the familiar warmth of his or her own home community. This represents a radical change from our former concept of removal of the patient to some point of isolation. While this new approach sounds very simple, it actually involves many ramifications of community planning, reorientation of professional thinking, new approaches to financing, and much more creative teamwork between the various professional disciplines and the lay volunteer.

That the planners and faculty for the symposium are well aware of the depth of this problem is made clear to me merely by examining the subject matter to be studied in these two days. I am particularly impressed by the topic of your closing session: "People as Individuals—Their Biological and Social Limits and Possibilities," because we know that solutions can be achieved only by people working together.

I am sure you realize that the Mental Health Association represents people—thousands upon thousands of volunteers, dedicated volunteers who have a vital concern regarding the subject matter which you will be discussing.

All of you are familiar with the Mental Health Association as a voluntary citizens' organization, but let me put some basic facts about our organization in capsule form for you. We are organized and active within 48 states, with over 900 chapters, and more than a million volunteers. This, as you can see, represents a substantial army of willing workers, capable of giving tremendous assistance to the professionals in the community if properly used. Based on the considerable experience I have had working with volunteers— and being one myself—I would be the first to say that volunteers can be of real help to professionals only if they are well recruited, properly trained, and adequately supervised.

We realize that we supplement, never *supplant;* but all of us must recognize the critical need for manpower in the broad field of mental illness.

This problem has become so acute that it now represents a mandate to you to make better use of volunteers.

The point of view of the medical profession is indeed broadening in this concept of mutual cooperation between lay citizens and medical professional. Let me cite one example with which many of you are familiar. Recently the American Medical Association, at its Second Congress on Mental Health in Chicago, placed emphasis on the fact that the general medical profession must join with volunteers in the fight against mental illness, acting both as physicians and private citizens.

I was impressed to see the American Medical Association in its First Congress identify mental illness as the major public health problem today. The AMA broadened its approach in the Second Congress to identify the urgent need for the whole medical profession, with specific emphasis on the general practitioner, to provide direct leadership in community-based action programs.

The Mental Health Association is firmly convinced that the medical profession will rise to this challenge and, through courses such as this symposium, equip itself with knowledge and understanding to provide the leadership that the rapidly expanding mental health program of today demands.

Let me tell you how I feel that we can work together. We must begin with the understanding that the professional by himself is not capable of taking care of the vast problems of mental illness unless the public is mobilized to develop and provide appropriate settings in which the physician can apply modern methods of treatment. In order to accomplish this massive public mobilization, it is essential to have an agency such as ours which understands the needs of the public and the potentials of the professional worker. This, then, is our role: to serve as a medium of interaction between the professional and the public.

We must work together, and you must learn to make effective use of us. You are familiar with the quotation: "No man is an island." We are truly beyond any age of insular thinking; and we are now engaged in a tremendous surge of cooperative accomplishment. Let us move ahead in common purpose, with the most commendable of goals—providing better care, near home, for the mentally ill.

SCOPE AND DIMENSIONS OF MENTAL HEALTH

INTRODUCTION

By Harry B. Friedgood, M.D., F.A.C.P.

To pave the way for the presentations which follow, I shall try to outline a theoretical concept which underlies and unifies these diverse fields of knowledge.

The term "mental health" is often used loosely, but generally it is meant to convey the idea of psychological well-being. This is true as far as it goes. However, one cannot think of psychological well-being, or of mental illness, merely in terms of what is going on in the minds of people. This would be meaningless, for man's psyche does not exist as an isolated mechanism in the universe of interrelated natural, biological, and psychosocial systems. The mind did not come into being in a vacuum, nor does it develop and function in a vacuum.

The mind is an integral part of the human organism's prenatal genetic and embryological experiences; and it is shaped postnatally by the march of events over the entire period of the individual's growth and maturation, biologically, socially, and culturally. Viewed in this light, character structure and personality may be regarded as "children" of the biological, social, and cultural environments which they have inherited from the past, and within which they are being nourished and developed in the present.

Biological, psychological, and sociocultural factors are inseparably integrated, so much so that they constitute an indivisible entity. Each component subsystem of this bio-psycho-social entity must be analyzed, evaluated, and quantified in relation to companion subsystems, as well as to the primary system in its entirety. I believe that one must look for meaningful insights into the nature of man and society in the *relationships* between component parts of this unitary system rather than in the *functional organization of the individual* components per se.

In attempting to visualize the possible nature of these relationships between biological, psychological, and social systems, I have found it helpful to apply to them, by analogy, the "field" and "energy" concepts native to the natural sciences.

Under ordinary conditions of life, the mind and the central nervous system, which is its anatomical and physiological home, appear to be in dynamic equilibrium with sociocultural and biological forces.

4

On the one hand, we may conceive of the mind and the central nervous system operating in a "field" where their growth, development, and patterns of function are constantly subject to the energy of sociocultural and biological forces. On the other hand, one may postulate that the energy of the mind and the central nervous system holds sway over biological and sociocultural forces and through them exercises a profound effect upon the course of events in living systems and in sociocultural systems, from the level of the family at home to that of nations abroad. Within recent decades, these interacting forces have tended to become unbalanced because they have grown erratically to staggering proportions, not only in terms of the crushing weight they bring to bear upon one another, but also in their ubiquity, which now extends from the outer space of the universe to the inner space of the molecule.

From this unitary point of view, it is a man's *way of life* which is ultimately the central theme of the so-called field of mental health. As a consequence, the mental health field is being peopled with multidisciplinary specialists who are concerned with the whole gamut of human biology, psychology, and sociology. This prodigious range of professional activity includes the realms of biological, social, and cultural structures, educational and religious institutions, political and economic systems, and the vast industrial and technological complex which has come to dominate mid-twentieth century civilization.

Obviously, within this universal frame of reference mental health personnel are called upon to do much more than look after the medical and social welfare of the emotionally disturbed and the mentally deranged—the objectives in the infancy of the mental health movement when Clifford Beers founded it under the guidance and encouragement of Dr. Adolf Meyer, Professor of Psychiatry at Johns Hopkins.

Mental illness is certainly the most glaring problem in the field of mental health, but it is by no means the most prevalent, or even the most pressing, from the standpoint of the far-reaching potential of the human mind for mischief as well as virtue.

The problems for society that arise from the emotionally disturbed or the fully unhinged mind are gargantuan. To cope with such problems effectively, one must develop an understanding and a working control of the biological, social, and cultural forces which shape the human mind and spirit from their inception. Scientists are already moving in this direction. Much of their momentum stems from the encouragement and financial assistance of citizens throughout the country, who work under the inspired leadership of people of Mrs. Winthrop Rockefeller's stature and dedication.

The foregoing considerations, taken together, suggest that it would fit the facts more comfortably if we were to think of the mental health field in the most comprehensive terms.

The field of mental health and the field of biological health are inseparable companions of the field of social health; and all three of them are integral components of a broader, unified area of human knowledge and endeavor which one might term *The Science of Man.*

A PSYCHIATRIC PERSPECTIVE

By M. ROBERT HARRIS, M.D.

The specialty of psychiatry does not hold a unified perspective or view-point regarding the field of mental health. Certainly "equal time" considera-tion should be given to the differing opinions and beliefs in this report, but as is known, the convictions of the spokesman often skew the data. Perhaps from the start it would be only fair to note that this presentation develops out of a strong community psychiatry-community mental health bias. As still another disclaimer, I would like to note that since the practice of psychiatry and mental health appropriately emphasizes a collaborative approach involving a large number of different professional and lay groups, it is somewhat inappropriate and difficult to speak only from the point of view of one of the participants.

The writings of Marie Jahoda,[1] Gerald Gurin, Joseph Veroff, and Sheila Feld,[2] and others have recently underlined the fact that our concepts and definitions of what constitutes mental health and even mental illness are varied, inconsistent, and difficult to standardize. In a type of security maneuver, we mental health practitioners have pointed to the fact that just as no completely acceptable all-inclusive concept or definition exists for physical health, so likewise none really exists for mental health or mental illness. However, from these gropings for specificity, certain guidelines and points of reference do seem to have emerged. Mental health, it is generally agreed, applies to an individual and the condition of an individual human mind, not as we occasionally less appropriately use the term to refer to a group, society, or culture. It is recognized that concepts and standards of mental health vary with the time, place, culture, and the expectations of the group. Many psychiatrists would support the concept that a definition of mental health cannot be established satisfactorily or solely on the criterion of *absence* of mental disease. This viewpoint is based upon value judgments which recognize gradations in utilizing individual capacities, experiencing satisfaction and happiness, as well as in establishing various individual levels of equilibrium and functional adaptation. However, other psychiatrists would regard this as a rather theoretical position and would state that for

[1]Jahoda, Marie: Current Concepts of Positive Mental Health, New York, Basic Books, 1958.

[2]Gerald Gurin, Joseph Veroff, and Sheila Feld: Americans View Their Mental Health, New York, Basic Books, 1960.

practical purposes, the absence of mental illness and the presence of mental health are congruent. Somewhat in the same vein, another positional statement would seem to be that good physical health is a necessary but not a *sufficient* or *exclusive* condition for mental health. In the parlance of the pollster, it is probably safe to say that "the majority of psychiatrists" would acknowledge that the mental health of an individual can only be assessed at any point in time by the consideration of a number of different, complex variables.

Most psychiatrists agree that the mental health of an individual is derived from a personality structure which incorporates simultaneously "healthy" and "unhealthy" aspects of personality organization and that one's functional position is determined at a point in time on a continuum ranging from mental illness to mental health through the assessment of a variety of factors. This is not a closed system, and the possibility exists for movement in either of the two directions.

However, our attention in this paper is not directed to the issue of mental health or mental illness as we assess it in the individual citizen. Rather our preoccupation is with the *field* of mental health which subsumes a broad and variously defined type of responsibility and concern for the emotional well-being and functioning of the total population. Again, when one considers the field of mental health, varieties of definitions exist. Mental health practices and the field of mental health are perceived by some to include *only* those issues, concerns, problems, and practices that have relevance to the "well" segment of the ill population. Mental health concerns would from this viewpoint include the multitude of living problems, stresses, and crises that trouble all citizens at some time but do not eventuate into overt psychiatric illnesses. A primary concern of the mental health group holding this concept would, of course, be the *prevention* of this transition to mental illness. Other individuals (including the author) perceive the field of mental health as the broad, inclusive responsibility for all that pertains to emotional and mental aspects of living and, therefore, would see the mental health area of concern encompassing the problems of the psychiatrically ill as well as those emotional issues confronting the "normal" population.

In contemplating the scope and dimensions of this field of mental health, psychiatry in the past decade has tended increasingly to emphasize and support a broad concept of mental health. Mental health services are perceived as needing to plan and carry out programs for reducing:

1. The incidence of mental disorders of all types in a community (Primary Prevention).

2. The duration of a significant number of those disorders which do occur (Secondary Prevention).

3. The impairment which may result from the disorders (Tertiary Prevention).

The recommendations of the Joint Commission on Mental Illness and Health in their final report[3] of 1961 have been criticized by some psychiatrists as focusing primarily upon the treatment of mental illness and not sufficiently upon prevention and indirect mental health services. As shall be mentioned later, this segment of the psychiatric population has been encouraged by the forthright charge to emphasize prevention that was included in President Kennedy's message to the Congress on February 5, 1963, regarding Mental Health Legislation.

In the past 20 years, certain guidelines have emerged concerning the scope and dimensions of community mental health practices, and, although these have now almost become professional litanies, they do seem pertinent to the subject under discussion here.

First, it seems necessary to briefly outline some of the characteristics of the psychiatric treatment which we are advocating and promoting.

1. Services should be physically and financially available when needed by the patient and his family.

2. Community mental health programs must provide appropriate and comprehensive services for all emotional disorders and not, for example, exclude the problems of children, mental retardation, delinquency, alcoholism, or the aged.

3. The treatment that is offered should be community based and in close proximity to the patient's home, family, friends, and employment.

4. A central treatment goal is the return of the patient as quickly as possible to a functioning capacity in his usual patterns of living.

5. Treatment programs should acknowledge, consider, and involve the family of patients or members of his familiar living unit.

6. Effective care requires the availability, utilization, and flexible coordination of a number of special forms of treatment and approaches at different phases of the treatment including, to name only a few:

    day hospitals
    emergency psychiatric clinics
    halfway houses
    sheltered workshops and employment services
    home visiting programs

7. Although appropriate *transitional treatment,* as stressed above, is necessary, *continuity of care* in program planning is also an important issue.

8. Active communication, collaborative planning, as well as consultation, must be built into the program with exchange of information facilitated among the variety of agencies and "helpers" whose contributions are so central to the real success of the treatment operation.

9. Although the service programs are designed with broad goals focusing

---

[3]Joint Commission on Mental Illness and Health: Action for Mental Health, New York, Basic Books, 1961.

upon the total population, they must be able to adapt to individual patients and not function rigidly out of the needs of the particular program or institution.

Important in psychiatry's point of view regarding the scope of mental health is the nature of what is perceived as the mental health responsibility. Much more, as stated above, this responsibility is recognized as encompassing the needs of a total population rather than continuing the pattern of treatment and help for only a partial segment of those for whom some sort of help or attention is important. This is increasingly obliging the professionals and nonprofessionals responsible for mental health to be aware of all elements of the community—all ages, classes, and ethnic groups. Certainly this is still an idealized goal and far from attained. However, it is at least being contemplated, discussed, and in various ways approached. This responsibility calls for participation from a variety of different levels—local, county, state, Federal; through private, public, and voluntary programs; as well as through the contribution of pre-need planning and insurance coverage. However, psychiatrists and other mental health specialists agree that a major part of this responsibility must be felt, assumed, and met by local planning and programming.

To serve the total mental health needs of the population, treatment programs must generally emphasize emergency treatment, short-term treatment, support, surmounting current crises, the re-establishment of a functional equilibrium, and the return of the patient to his community, rather than intensive psychotherapy with goals directed toward the total reorganization of personality. Psychiatrists are studying the Joint Commission's conclusion that a new group of therapists must be trained, in addition to increasing the number of those from the traditional psychiatric disciplines. This is a controversial recommendation and one about which there is as yet no agreement. Certainly, the profession from psychiatry's viewpoint must intensify its research investment, basic as well as applied, and vigorously pursue treatment evaluation and follow-up studies.

In order to be effective in community mental health practice, it seems apparent that the psychiatrist must acquire greater knowledge about a wide range of issues concerning biological, social, political, economic, and governmental aspects of the community and nation. He has to become more aware of the large number of other professional and nonprofessional workers who offer or may, if enlisted, offer independent or collaborative help in dealing with the health, educational, legal, and social aspects of the problems of the "well," the mentally ill, and the retarded. Many problems need not and should not involve the psychiatric professionals. Traditionally, the psychiatrist has worked fairly comfortably and cooperatively with psychologists, social workers, rehabilitation therapists, nurses, and other physicians. The new team must expand now to include social scientists, economists, legislators, citizens, public health personnel, welfare workers, religious personnel, the police, educational groups, and many others. Increasingly, psychiatrists are acknowledging that the responsibility for promoting mental health necessitates a comprehensive approach in which the mentally disordered patterns of citizens are seen as a part of a whole system of ecological responses of a population in its interactions with its environment. This new emphasis shared by psychiatry with many other disciplines and groups would seem to require that we not only study mental disease but give attention also to many aspects of man's role in society.

Psychiatrists have accepted a broader responsibility for consultation in the mental health field and are offering consultation to a number of different helpers and caretakers who are working directly with mental health needs and problems. These groups include teachers, ministers, general practitioners, lawyers, police, employers, corporation heads, public health nurses, legislators, administrators, volunteers, and others. Although a few sentences back, it was rather glibly stated that psychiatrists collaborated fairly comfortably with other physicians, most psychiarists are quite aware that we must strive to improve these relationships and to particularly find better methods of helping and encouraging the general practitioner in the important role he plays (or must play) in the community's mental health. The Second American Medical Association National Congress in Mental Illness and Health held in November 1964 in Chicago emphasized the importance of involving all physicians, not just psychiatrists, in emerging mental health programs.

Acknowledging the important responsibility that exists for developing professional manpower, a large number of psychiatric training centers have recently introduced special training programs designed to help equip our psychiatrists of the future to practice in this area of community psychiatry. The Langley Porter Community Mental Health Training program is an example of this type of specialized psychiatric training.

Although this interest and involvement of psychiatry in broad aspects of social and community affairs is increasing, there are a number of psychiatrists[4-8] who have vigorously spoken out recently about their concerns that

[4]Branch, C. H. Hardin: Have Plan, Will Travel: Planning Mental Health Programs. Summary of a Regional Western Interstate Commission for Higher Education Conference at Portland, Oreg., Feb. 16-19, 1964.

[5]Grinker, Roy R., Sr.: Psychiatry rides madly in all directions. Arch. Gen. Psychiat. 10: 228-237.

[6]Ross, Mathew: Community psychiatry as an opportunity for medical leadership. Arch. Gen. Psychiat. 3: 478-489.

in this move psychiatrists are going too far afield. They question the psychiatrists' qualifications for making useful and helpful contributions in these areas and most of all stress that certainly not all the problems confronting man are psychiatric.

Perhaps one of the better statements delineating psychiatry's point of view regarding the scope and dimensions of mental health is actually embodied in the concept of the community mental health center. The mental health center program was established in October 1963 when the 88th Congress enacted Public Law 88-164, "Mental Retardation Facilities and Community Mental Health Centers Construction Act of 1963."

Much information about these model programs is easily available, and it seems appropriate here to address myself to only a very few of the central features of the program. The "center" concept does not refer to, or emphasize, the erection of a new building which would roof all needed mental health services. Rather the center is a functioning, enabling, and coordinating agency which draws upon existing programs, eliminating gaps and lack of continuity in service which occur when separate community psychiatric services function in an unrelated manner. All components need not and will not be housed under one roof. Sponsorship and planning for each center reverts to each community, and the resulting program should reflect each community's particular needs, its existing services, and its ability to mobilize interest and involvement. This is a cooperative program and, for example, draws heavily upon the contributions of general practitioners, private psychiatrists, and a variety of other disciplines and community programs in the endeavor.

Clearly the Mental Health Center regulations require that: "Programs must take into consideration the needs of all age groups, assure continuity of care for patients and assure that the relationship between the individual elements of the services promotes continuity of care and proper sharing of treatment information." The Mental Health Center program also emphasizes preventive services, as well as consultation, research, evaluation, and training.

Although psychiatrists are generally aware that much effort, development, implementation, evaluation, and modification of the program for community mental health centers must yet occur, there is, however, satisfaction in knowing that legislation and planning have been accomplished which generally embody our current points of view regarding mental health services.

[7]Halleck, Seymour and Miller, Milton: Psychiatric consultation: questionable social precedents of some current practices. Amer. J. Psychiat. 120 (4): 164-169.

[8]Stainbrook, Edward: Psychotherapy and the community organization of the helping response to distress and illness. Unpublished paper presented at APA Meeting, May 1964, Los Angeles.

A SOCIOLOGICAL PERSPECTIVE

By JOHN A. CLAUSEN, PH.D.

Let us start with the simple postulate that mental disorder is a major social problem in contemporary society, and mental health, a major value for large segments of our society. Mental illness, both as concept and as phenomenon, has been of much greater interest to social scientists than has mental health. There are probably a number of reasons for this, but the one I want to stress relates to the meanings of the two concepts in terms of social action. For most people, "mental health" connotes either a vaguely conceived state of psychological well-being or is simply a euphemism for concern with mental disorder. But mental disorder is that which leads people to behave incomprehensibly—and therefore to draw sanctions against themselves, one of which entails being locked up in mental hospitals.

Sociologists have been concerned with a number of different facets of the problem of mental disorder. One major interest is evidenced by their participation in community studies attempting to establish the effects of particular life conditions upon the prevalence of mental disorder. This topic can be approached either by studying who is treated by psychiatrists or sent to mental hospitals for prolonged care or by interviewing a cross section of the population and then securing psychiatric evaluation of the interview protocols. Whichever approach one takes, there is quite consistent evidence that the lower the social status of a particular segment of the population, the higher the proportion of persons in that segment who are regarded by psychiatrists as showing manifestations of psychiatric disorder. Again, the lower the status, the higher the proportion of persons who are sent to mental hospitals as a means of dealing with their problems. I wish shortly to return to a more detailed consideration of the findings of these studies relating social background to the prevalence of psychiatric disorders. But let me get on with my brief cataloging of sociological concerns in the field of mental health. Sociologists have also been much involved in studies of institutions for the care of mental patients—with staff-patient relationships, with the sorting and evaluation of patients, and with the discrepancies between the mass processing of patients and the objectives of a therapeutic approach to mental illness. Closely related to the topics already mentioned, is a consideration of public attitudes toward mental illness and of the ways in which various members of the population react and respond to the behaviors that are labeled "mental illness." Despite some heartening changes

13

in the past decade or so, both public attitudes and public hospitals still leave much to be desired from the standpoint of the mental patient.

I wish now to take as my point of departure the findings of two of the most sophisticated and recent of the major studies of the prevalence of mental illness. One—the Midtown Manhattan Project[1]—was concerned with establishing the prevalence of psychiatric symptomatology in a densely populated part of our largest city. The other—the Stirling County Project[2] —sought to do the same thing for a small city and its predominantly rural county in one of Canada's maritime provinces. Both studies concluded that the vast majority of persons assessed manifested some symptoms of emotional disturbance. Perhaps this is not much different from saying that almost all of us at some time or other suffer from respiratory infections or mild illnesses and disabilities without being seriously incapacitated. But both the Midtown Project and the Stirling County Project suggested that from one-fifth to one-fourth of the total population of adults in the areas studied were *significantly* impaired in their functioning by virtue of psychiatric disorder.

Both studies indicated that the prevalence of psychiatric disorder was much higher among persons in the lower strata of socioeconomic status than among the more well-to-do. Thus, in the lowest stratum of population in the New York study, 47 per cent of the respondents were regarded as significantly impaired in their functioning by virtue of psychiatric symptoms, and 10 per cent were regarded as completely incapacitated. The Stirling County study produced very similar findings, nearly 50 per cent being rated as having psychiatric disorder with significant impairment among residents of the most depressed areas of the county. The similarity in findings would seem to suggest that whatever the source of the psychiatric disorders noted in the deprived segments of the population, they cannot be attributed to life conditions or to a sorting of the population that is unique to New York City or to cities in general. What is perhaps unique to New York City is the level of treatment services available to those desiring psychiatric treatment. Among well-to-do persons who were rated significantly impaired in the Midtown study, fully one-fifth were receiving outpatient treatment at the time of the study and an additional one-third had at some time or other been in treatment. At the lower status levels, however, only one per cent of the persons regarded as significantly impaired by virtue of psychiatric symptoms were currently receiving treatment of any kind.

These findings seem to indicate something of the scope and dimensions of the problem of mental health. Perhaps it would be more accurate to say

---

[1]Strole, Leo et al.: Mental Health in the Metropolis. New York, McGraw Hill, 1961.

[2]Leighton, Dorothea et al.: The Character of Danger. New York, Basic Books, 1964.

that they seem to me to pose a dilemma for those concerned with mental health. How can one begin to cope with a problem of such magnitude? Certainly not by attempting to go out and build and staff mental health clinics or community mental health centers in the areas with the most acute problems. Indeed, before attempting to do anything, it seems imperative that we examine the assumption that the best way to deal with psychiatric disorders of the type found among the deprived and depressed populations in Midtown and Stirling County is to provide psychiatric services. I do not mean to suggest that services do not have to be made more readily available for defining and treating severe psychoneurosis and psychosis in these populations. I do believe, however, that the appropriate way of seeking to cut down the symptomatology so manifest in deprived segments of the population is not psychiatry, but skill training and economic opportunity.

Far more than in the era before World War II we now recognize that mental health cannot be divorced from position in the social structure. The Supreme Court acted on the matter of school segregation when it was no longer possible to doubt that segregation was psychologically damaging to the excluded population. Two-thirds of a century of detailed studies of life in urban slums, dating from Booth's *Life and Labor of the People of London,* had documented the prevalence of a host of problems of social pathology before there was sophisticated examination of the psychological consequences of the deprivation and devaluation experienced by the underprivileged. Now we recognize a direct relationship between deprivation and alienation from the goals of the larger society, feelings of powerlessness, distrust of others, apathy. Further, with the advent of large-scale surveys of the epidemiology of mental illness, we find a very high relationship between what psychiatrists regard as symptoms of mental disorder and what sociologists characterize as anomie or normlessness—precisely this feeling of distrust, disenchantment, and lack of relatedness to the larger social order.

Obviously, this does not mean that mental health is the primary problem of the deprived. *One consequence* of deprivation is the kind of attitudes, adjustment patterns, and psychophysiological symptoms that are indicative of poor mental health. In my opinion, the primary reason for tackling problems of deprivation is not mental health, any more than that the primary reason for providing good housing is to enhance physical health. The point I want to make is that a major source of psychiatric symptomatology appears to be one facet of a larger social problem—a problem entailing human indignity, wasted resources, self-perpetuating misery. To define the problem as primarily one of mental health would be offensive to the persons involved and on the whole a fruitless way of using scarce mental health resources. Some of those resources should be used for research on the best means of meeting the kinds of needs that are manifest, and for trial or demonstration projects. Further, persons interested in mental health ought to be supporters of strong social action against deprivation and devaluation of any group within the population. Parenthetically, one must anticipate that the solution to major problems of deprivation is not likely to come about exclusively or perhaps even primarily through the actions of persons who are balanced, reasonable, and realistic. Almost all social movements mounted against profound injustice have gotten at least some of their impetus from people who have seemed implacably angry, hostile, and unreasonable.

I have argued that mental health resources should not be diverted to the massive provision of clinical psychiatric services for deprived populations. This may seem to be a strange plea from a sociologist, since sociologists are continually pointing at the discrepancies between psychiatric care available to the affluent and the poor. What I am asserting is that the problem will not yield to clinical services. Certainly we need to provide better facilities, better care for the mentally ill in all parts of the population. Particularly at the lowest status levels, we need a different approach from that which has prevailed. The whole mode of dealing with life problems is vastly different from that taken for granted in the middle class.

Like many sociologists, I have profound ambivalence about the terms "mental health" and "mental illness." Quite clearly, mental disorder is unlike any other form of illness, in that its primary manifestations entail the distortion of symbolic processes and the disruption of even the most intimate interpersonal ties. A major dilemma is posed by the fact that the person needing help may be the last one to acknowledge such need. Further, we know from a number of studies that, in general, the seeking of psychiatric help is likely to lead to devaluation by one's peers. Going to a psychiatrist is still widely regarded as an admission of inadequacy, unless one happens to belong to that small segment of our society which has been called "friends of psychotherapy." Again the implication is that we need to find quite different modes of providing service when we do attempt to establish community mental health services for the entire population. To some extent mental health services can be incorporated in other medical facilities, without using any psychiatric terminology, since a very high proportion of the persons with psychiatric symptoms number psychophysiological difficulties among those symptoms. Perhaps though, there are kinds of skill training that can be offered without implying that those in need of skills are inadequate or ill.

Alternatives to current clinical approaches are needed, but this does not mean that persons most acutely in need of psychiatric help are now being adequately cared for. In my opinion they are not. Psychiatrists are physicians, and one expects physicians to take care of those who are ill—even though one may look forward to the day when the physician's primary role is keeping his clients well. But only a tiny fraction of our qualified psychiatrists are now employed in hospitals for the long-term care of the mentally ill. Another very small proportion is involved in clinics and psychiatric wards where acutely disturbed persons may receive prompt help. A number of communities have developed facilities for dealing with mental health emergencies, but I doubt very much whether any community has a setup for psychiatric emergencies that is at all comparable with what it affords for victims of automobile accidents. I want to argue strongly for the greater use of psychiatric resources for dealing with acute, severe mental illness. This is not to deny that psychiatrists can be very helpful to persons with a variety of problems of living; it is rather to assert that some problems are more acute than others—and are also more appropriately defined as problems of mental health and illness.

The symptoms of mental disorder have been interpreted in many ways— as possession by the devil, as indicative of being a witch, as mental illness, and as problems of living. I do not think that mental illness is a myth, though I should prefer not to use the term "mental illness" for those conditions that seem to be primarily matters of poor training in interpersonal relations and attendant difficulties in living. It is true that such difficulties —like illness—are not to be blamed upon the individuals who experience them, but derive from conditions the individual did not create. The primary task in helping such persons is to motivate them to want to help themselves, and I doubt very much that this can best be done by telling them they are sick.

In conclusion, then, I would emphasize that in considering the scope and dimensions of mental health we must be aware of the implications of the labels that we use and must consider alternative strategies for achieving our objectives.

A REACTIONARY PERSPECTIVE

By HENRY S. MAAS, PH.D.

One approach in defining the scope and dimensions of mental health as a human condition is to question the utility of any such endeavor. Mental health is also the designation of a social action movement. Such movements, it can be demonstrated, prosper when their goals are kept imprecise and their boundaries fluid. Mental health is, in addition, a euphemistic title for a field within which professional persons concerned with the treatment of mental illness and research on its causes and correlated conditions can meet and exchange ideas. But such professional workers have little practical use, as I see it, for high-level abstractions on the nature of mental health. They need to have criteria for assessing the improvement of their patients or for selecting controls for their research in psychopathology. But the starting points for such measurements are logically the dimensions of the forms of psychopathology under consideration and not the dimensions of mental health.

Efforts toward clarifying ideas in practice and research are hardly furthered by statements like the following: "Mental health used to mean its opposite, mental disease; now it means not just health but human well-being."[1] This quotation echoes a sentiment, if not an idea, which might have been extracted in essence, if not in the same words slightly rearranged, from any of possibly 100 different recent public pronouncements. In the forum of the mental health movement it has a quite justifiable place. Social action thrives on such shibboleths. Science and professional practice, however, can only be befuddled by them and appropriately reject them. Social action, under such rallying calls, attracts increasing numbers of people, and with the growth in size of a social movement its influence is likely to grow too, and its public policy and organizational ambitions are more likely to be realized. The relationships, however, between (1) treatment programs and research and (2) the mental health movement as a social actionist force have not, to my knowledge, ever been adequately analyzed. The needs for conceptualization in the two arenas seem to me quite different. And where confusions between the two have occurred, unfortunate unanticipated consequences have resulted.

Mental health itself is not a field of practice or research. There is no

---

[1] Nicholas Hobbs: Mental health's third revolution. Amer. J. Orthopsychiat. 34: 824, 1964.

theory of mental health to guide either enterprise, but rather separate disciplines collaborate on problems in this field. In whose language, then, might we define scope and dimensions? Learning the language of those disciplines through participation in the mental health movement, more-over, does not qualify one for membership in any discipline, for each dis-cipline has a body of knowledge and techniques, whether in practice or research, far larger than that part of the discipline at work on mental health problems. Nor does experience in practice qualify one for partici-pation in research any more than experience in research qualifies one for participation in practice. The fluidity of boundaries and the changing nature of short-term aims, if not long-range goals, which keep a social movement vital and effective, provide inappropriate models for the organi-zation of professional practice and the scientific underpinnings of the move-ment. Against any such proposition, charges of concern about professional hegemony, guild controls, and territoriality, and of resistance to change are likely to be raised, loud and angrily. And yet I wonder whether failures to distinguish among various segments of the mental health field, and roles within it, and careers preparatory to these roles, have not confused others as well as ourselves.

May I illustrate a few of my points, in good clinical fashion, by examin-ing a case in some detail. About three decades ago, Kingsley Davis analyzed 13 publications of the mental hygiene movement, as of the 1920's and early 30's, and concluded that mental hygiene promulgated, as criteria of mental health, such personal attributes as ambition, competitiveness, conformity, individual responsibility, prudence, and worldly asceticism.[2] These, he main-tained, allied mental hygiene with the Protestant Ethic and understandably so. For, he continued, his analysis of *Who's Who* type data on the lives of 51 leaders of the mental hygiene movement revealed them to be "of the type one would expect to uphold the Protestant principles—mostly upper middle-class professionals, predominantly of British ancestry—who are idealistic, respectable, and capable, and on the side of humanitarian in-dividualism."[3]

These findings troubled Davis, as a social scientist, on at least two explicit counts. One was that: "In so far as the mental hygienist retains his ethical system, he misses a complete scientific analysis of his subject and hence fails to use the best technological means to his applied-science goals."[4] By this time, at the very end of his paper, Davis had forgotten his opening-sentence distinction between mental hygiene as a social move-

---

[2] Kingsley, Davis: Mental hygiene and the class structure, Psychiatry 1: 55-65, 1938. (See especially pp. 57-58).

[3] *Ibid.,* p. 58.

[4] *Ibid.,* p. 65.

ment and as an "applied science" and related his findings on the former to the latter. The argument I am advancing is that a successful mental health movement appropriately sets as mental health criteria attributes which are consonant with the changing contemporaneous values of a society—provided that they are on the side of humanitarianism. That the mental health movement seems to be doing something like this is suggested at least by the out-dated character of the attributes Davis listed 30 years ago. Today we should have a very different list. And for social action purposes, the movement might lose much of its adaptability if it searched for and settled on clear-cut and absolute definitions of the scope and dimensions of mental health. Concerned with, for example, generating public support for new facilities and services for the mentally ill and preventive programs in this field (perhaps as professional judgments and scientific findings indicate the probable utility and effectiveness of such), the mental health movement might well have lost its impetus and zeal if it had adopted the scientific amorality Kingsley Davis urged upon it in the 1930's.

But Davis had a second objection to what he found. As a sociologist, he was troubled by the field's "individualism" and its "psychologistic" perspectives. He concluded that "mental hygiene seems to be limping along on one foot. . ." because of what he considered "mental hygiene's neglect of social process" and of the social determinants of mental disorder.[5] There were by then, in the literature, reports on the ecological studies of Faris and Dunham and the related work of other Chicago urban sociologists— Robert Park, Clifford Shaw, Louis Wirth, and others—as well as contemporaneous anthropological contributions to mental health. Davis was thus on firm ground in arguing that social science had something to add, and in a quite different theoretical context from the "struggle between individual and society" which Freud described in Civilization and its Discontents.[6] But Davis failed to distinguish, again, between the implications of social science perspectives and findings for the mental health movement and for the separate service and research disciplines which contribute ideas to the movement.

It was the movement's very vagueness of concepts and ill-boundaried limits in the 30's which permitted it in the 40's to admit not only new ideas and aims but also their heralds. If Kingsley Davis complained as an outsider in 1938 that sociology had been given little attention by mental hygienists, Lawrence K. Frank announced, very much as a long-standing insider, in 1948 that the Preparatory Commission for the International

[5]Op. cit., p. 62.

[6]Sigmund Freud: Civilization and its Discontents. New York, Jonathan Cope & Harrison Smith, 1930, p. 136.

Congress on Mental Health had considered its problems from the points of view of seven disciplines, and his catalog began with sociology.[7] In short, in less than a decade the formerly uninvited had risen to the head of the guest list. How would Kingsley Davis explain such professional mobility in face of the deep-rooted commitment to individualism he saw in those who then held power in the mental hygiene movement? It would seem, rather, that the very imprecision of the definitions of goals and of the "psychologistic" concepts guiding the movement, which Davis had attacked, kept the movement open to newcomers and helped to make their ascendancy possible. Had the scope and dimensions of mental hygiene or mental health been carefully defined or delimited at that time, sociologists and their eye-opening perspectives* might have been excluded from the field. Amorphous boundaries and conceptual fuzziness would appear to be functional in such a public arena.

But do we need greater clarity about the scope and dimensions of mental health for the disciplines engaged in practice and research? I am arguing that still, now, more than definitions of the outer limits and inner elements of mental health, we need precisely these to be ramified and detailed for mental illness, in its multiple forms and contexts, and specifically in relation to diverse and new methods of treatment. But confusions between the

---

[7]Lawrence K. Frank and J. R. Rees: Foreword, Statement by International Preparatory Commission. London, International Congress on Mental Health, August, 1948, p. ii.

*Some sociological observations focus on "field" where psychologists have formerly seen only "figure." The effect is sometimes one of shock or delight at discovery and sometimes irritation with the perverse denial of mental illness as biopsychic processes. (See, for example, Erving Goffman. *Asylums: Essays on the Social Situation of Mental Patients and Other Inmates.* Garden City, New York, Doubleday-Anchor Books, 1961.) Lest, however, it be thought that the only relationship between the social sciences and the field of mental health has been that of donor and recipient, one must recall, for example, the mutual exchange of ideas among psychiatrist Harry Stack Sullivan, anthropologist Edward Sapir, political scientist Harold D. Lasswell, and Chicago sociologists, the personal history of which is found in Helen Swick Perry's "Introduction" to Harry Stack Sullivan, *The Fusion of Psychiatry and Social Science,* New York: Norton, 1964. Kingsley Davis' paper (*op. cit.*) had its publication in the first issue of the journal *Psychiatry,* which was founded as a result of Sullivan's collaborative exchanges with social scientists during the very period Davis had under scrutiny. Of this development Davis, in his footnote 33, remarks only that "Psychiatry is waking up to the necessity of studying interpersonal relations," citing Sullivan's May, 1937, *American Journal of Sociology* paper, but failing to credit Sullivan for writing as a psychiatrist "on the implications of psychiatry . . . for investigations in the social sciences." By contrast, in the same first issue of *Psychiatry,* Edward Sapir contributed a paper entitled, "Why Cultural Anthropology Needs the Psychiatrist."

banners of social action and the business of professional service and research have befuddled and diverted us.

In the name of mental health, persons trained in psychotherapy have entered the ranks of city planners, while persons whose heritage is in social group work and community organization in neighborhood centers—where the new war on poverty still needs them—are treating groups of patients on psychiatric wards. Persons trained in nursery school education (plus a summer's T-group experience) are badly needed in preschool services of all kinds and in pressure groups for the expansion of day-care centers and educational units for the "culturally deprived," but they are teaching "normal" parents how to interact "normally" with their "normal" children, toward the presumed ends of mental health. Persons trained in sociology are arguing against urban renewal projects which dislocate old neighbors; when the latter understandably resist removal from their accustomed but rat-infested slums, the sociologists' diagnosis is that they are suffering damage to their mental health.[8] Priorities near the level of survival may be seen to vary with varying theoretical perspectives, but appeals or attacks on the grounds of mental health need to be based in an understanding of human adaptive mechanisms under stress and of psychopathology in its extremes, as limited and inferential as our knowledge of such basically bio-psychic processes may be.*

[8]Marc Fried: "Grieving for a Lost Home." In *The Urban Community: People and Policy in the Metropolis* (Leonard J. Duhl, editor). New York, Basic Books, 1963, pp. 151-171. Setting aside questions about the form of the interview (see footnote, pp. 154-155) in this West End Boston study of urban relocated men and women who report "feelings of sadness or depression," one must remember that a reported feeling of sadness is not, itself, symptomatic of any of the mental illnesses named "depression." More specifically, few clinically trained workers are likely to find in the "prototypical" case example of the Figella family (pp. 161-162) "a severe grief reaction," for, even on the level of reported data, "they continue in close contact with many people" and "they have always maintained a very close marital relationship . . . ."

*In the lexicon of the mental health movement, transitional unhappiness may mistakingly be equated with incipient mental illness. Science requires greater rigor of both definition and evidence. In fact, the numerous demographic and culture and personality studies, which seem to establish a positive if gross relationship between social change and mental illness (and especially psychomatic disorders), need to be followed up with more refined investigations. The findings of psychological experiments on sensory deprivation and social isolation, in which psychoticlike symptoms result from *lack* of changing stimuli, suggest that we probably have a bimodal relationship between degree of situational change and extent of pathological response. If so, then we need to clarify how extensive or enduring either rapid social change or its obverse (no change) must be for biopsychic damage to occur; and then, more specifically, we need to discover both how enduring the damage is and what biopsychic predispositions are necessary for differential responses to occur in differ-

Thus, we are beginning what may become massive diversions from the central foci and spheres of competence and knowledge in a number of disciplines, all with serious manpower shortages. Some of these shifts in focus—especially the flight of those informed about mental illness away from it—have the character of denial or surrender, but none of the apparent utility of the legerdemain with language which provided the mental health movement with its most recent name.

There are many disciplines which deal with theories of psychopathology, and provide in addition larger substantive contexts within which psychopathology and its determinants may be understood. There is no single discipline of psychopathology, but knowledge of it is a part of many disciplines, and perspectives on its complexities vary. Some of these disciplines, like psychiatry, within its medical context, include education in diagnostic and treatment knowledge and skills. Like psychiatry are clinical psychology and psychiatric social work, each part of a larger heritage and focus which its students are taught, and each providing a supervised field work or internship program as part of the novice's professional training.* Other disciplines like sociology and anthropology contain fields of specialized knowledge bearing on mental illness, and include also training in research techniques relevant to the development of knowledge in these disciplines. The research techniques are no more interchangeable with the therapeutic techniques than the latter are with the former. The understanding of psychopathology which comes of research interviews with, for example, the families of the mentally ill hardly provides a basis for assessing incipient pathology in their neighbors' children. Correlates, as we all know but sometimes forget, are not

---

*Within these practice disciplines, overtraining in traditional methods is likely to reduce the profession's capacity to create and develop radically new treatment approaches. Education in practice should probably therefore occur in a milieu which, if not permeated by scientific scepticism, still is a questioning and experimental one. Such an approach makes clear that presently taught and used methods have evolved out of less satisfactory ones, just as tomorrow's methods will be different, and perhaps radically so, from today's. The argument that practice disciplines are themselves maintainers of the status quo fails to accommodate the historical evidence of changes which have occurred within such disciplines—and of which apprentices need always to be made aware by masters who never forget such changes. The impatient who would throw over traditional disciplines stand to lose, in the process, the knowledge bases and heritages which give treatment agents strength vis-a-vis the weakness of the mentally ill.

---

ent individuals, in response to externally identical stressful situations. Some of the literature on crisis and social stressors suggests that successful coping is ego-strengthening. If so, then, for what kinds of human organism in what kinds of situations? To recommend against planned social change on the grounds of existing social science evidence is to act prematurely on theoretically too limited and substantively inadequate evidence.

always causes. And confusions between independent and dependent variables can lead to misinterpretations not only in research but also in the lives of people.

If we have no science of psychopathology, per se, we have not even the vaguest beginnings of a science of mental health. Nor, at present, should we head in this direction. The strongest arguments against the former apply also to the latter. They are along the lines that Reader and Goss[9] advanced in their analysis of the status of medical sociology a few years ago: ". . . the optimal research contribution the sociologist may make to medicine for some time to come consists of using the scientific method in pursuing studies which are based upon and add to sociological theory. This does not mean shunning collaboration with physicians or avoiding investigations of so-called practical problems. It does mean that such problems need to be examined in terms of their more general sociological significance, for maximal benefit to medicine and to sociology."[10] The counsel that maximum benefits will accrue "if the sociologist who does research in medicine remains a sociologist first and foremost" is based in the assumption that otherwise he will be cut off from the lifelines to his knowledge and the potential uniqueness of his contributions. The equalizing and homogenizing effects of a popular movement will be lost if these influences carry over to their members in their professional service and research roles. And those segments of the service and research professions that have traditionally focused on the problems of the mentally ill should be aware if they are using a kind of magical thinking when they assume that patients will recover or their suffering will be contained or spread no further because these specialists are now working for "mental health."

---

[9]George G. Reader and Mary E. W. Goss: The sociology of medicine. In Sociology Today: Problems and Prospects (Robert K. Merton, Leonard Broom and Leonard S. Cottrell, Jr., editors). New York, Basic Books, 1959, pp. 229-246.

[10]*Ibid,* p. 246.

THE FUNDAMENTAL ISSUES

Editors' Note:

The following section is devoted to some special contributions of the disciplines of psychiatry and psychoanalysis, psychology and sociology to the fundamental issues involved in the struggle toward mental health. Dr. Reed Brockbank's psychoanalytic approach emphasizes the vicissitudes of the maturation and development of the individual's sense of identity. Dr. Walcott Beatty looks at various environmental influences on "mentally health learning." He describes these influences on the learning of *coping mechanisms, autonomy,* and *expressive ability.* Dr. Ralph Lane writes of the contribution of the social conditions, in which individuals live and learn, in the development of emotional well-being.

PROBLEMS OF SELF-IDENTITY IN MENTAL ILLNESS AND MENTAL HEALTH

By Reed Brockbank, M.D.

The most significant quality distinguishing humans from other animal species is "self-consciousness" or the ability to conceptualize awareness of one's self as a separate, coherent entity. For centuries philosophers, biologists, and social scientists have turned their attention to the phenomena of self-consciousness and to the multifarious aspects of individual and group identity. These have included the polar problems of individualization and collectivism, isolation and intimacy, autonomy and symbiosis. In recent years psychiatrists and psychoanalysts have become increasingly aware that these phenomena raise some of the most fundamental issues in the problem of mental illness and mental health.

Man's self-consciousness causes him to ask, "Who am I?" or "What am I?" or "How did I come to be what I am?" A much more disturbing question and one that he only occasionally allows to enter his consciousness is "How do I *know* that I *am?*" This question is usually passed over with the preconscious reassurance, "I *feel* my existence." But what about those occasions when, even though awake and conscious, one may not feel this certainty of continued unitary existence of body and mind.

In psychiatric practice the frequently observed loss of the sense of identity in the psychotic individual who says, "I am dead" or "My body is dissolving," represents only the end stage of a severe disturbance in the sense of self. This extreme feeling of loss of one's existence is at one end of a continuum of uncertainties that may be observed not only in the mentally ill but also in the normal adolescent who struggles characteristically to "find himself," in the young adult who can't decide on his future "role" in life or is uncertain about his role as a sexual and intimate love partner, in the middle-aged who are uncertain about their role as parental figures with a solid identity to pass on to their children, in the elderly who are uncertain about their acceptance and status, particularly when strong and persistent regression to childhood feelings occur.

The adolescent struggling with identity diffusion attempts to bolster his sense of identity in a group. He feels secure when he is most like the others in his group. Some schizophrenics, on the other hand, and some prepsychotic individuals find the group threatening to their shaky sense of identity and will avoid it or approach it with increased anxiety and fear lest they "lose themselves in the group." Others with predominantly narcissistic person-alities also reject groups and avoid them for similar reasons. When such an individual finds himself in a group, he will often overemphasize his difference from all others, his uniqueness, his need to be the center of attention so that he will not be lost in the collective body. His anxiety in such a situation may be so great that he will invite rejection by the group or even by society at large, which labels him "egocentric," "too self-centered," or "too demand-ing." He prefers this to taking a chance on losing his sense of self. Yet such an individual also knows, as does the adolescent, that his self-identity can be bolstered by contact and identification with the group, provided it is a stable one and does not itself change too rapidly or too radically; or he may identify with a single other person who loves and cares for him and from whom he can replenish his partially impoverished ego with a new source of libido.

Paul Federn was an early psychoanalyst who had a particular interest in the problem of the *sense of self* and its vicissitudes. Since he perceptively called attention to disturbances and uncertainties in the sense of self as a significant factor in psychotic and prepsychotic ego states, a considerable amount of study has been done to determine just how self-identity develops. In this presentation I will outline briefly some of the insights that have been gained into this developmental sequence. I will draw heavily on the tentative conclusions made by Renee Spitz from his direct observations of infants.

Federn's concept of "ego feeling" (*Erlebnis*) refers to a subjective experi-ence that may be felt by anyone, and this experience he believed was proof of the existence of the ego as a functioning psychic structure. In the normal state, we are seldom aware of our self or ego feeling; but we become acutely aware of its existence, like that of the air we breathe, when we are partially deprived of it. Thus, in states of depersonalization there is an acute lack of the awareness of the sense of self; and when this lack is severe there may be a feeling that one is dead or "no longer myself." This stage represents a subjective awareness of the disruption of the ego. In such normal situations, such as temporary states of exhaustion or just before falling asleep, one may feel a temporary loss of one's position in space or of the reality of objects in the external world—that is, a mild loss of what Federn calls "bodily ego feelings." Such fleeting sensations of a loss of the sense of reality of a body part or dissociation of a certain organ from the self are frequent and are regarded as normal occurrences.

The "mental ego feeling" (*Erlebnis*) or sense of self has a complex devel-opmental history in the human. For the first two months of life the average human infant functions without awareness of self or outside world. He responds to stimuli in a reflex manner and elementary conditioning begins to take place. This is called the undifferentiated or nondifferentiated stage. The first significant development in self-awareness takes place sometime during the third month when the infant responds with a smile showing an affective response and recognition of a face as an external object apart from himself. This is his first perception of an external world. Spitz called it the first psychic organizer. Thus, the outside world has begun to be differentiated in the mind of the infant from his global sense of unity with the world around. This does not mean specific recognition of any one person as separate from another, or even the differentiation of animate from inanimate objects, but it is the beginning of what will gradually become the awareness of the difference between "me" and "not me." Along with this development comes the capacity to lay down memory traces, thinking, and the development of what Freud called the reality principle. This represents the beginning of psychic structure.

The second major developmental change occurs around eight months, when the infant begins to differentiate one external object from another. The figure of the mother takes on a specific meaning, and there can be no substitution for her without the immediate development of anxiety. Other areas of discrimination and differentiation have, of course, taken place during this period. Thought processes and true object relations with affective responses attached are developed. The third developmental stage separates the human species from the lower primates. This is the acquisition of the ability to communicate by the use of verbal symbols. At this time (around 18 months) the human is in a position to conceptualize distinctly the awareness of self. The proof of this development is the child's use of the "no" gesture, at first to the mother as a separate person, and later the verbal use of "no" to the self which has now become a separate and distinct entity. The experiences of weaning, walking, talking, falling, and touching, first the self then the other (not self), further solidifies this sense of separateness, and symbiosis is gradually replaced with autonomy.

From the above observation of epigenetic development, it is clear that the sense of self is part of a gradually evolving process of ego differentiation. Beginning with the third month of life there is an awareness of an outside world. This comes about through the loving attachment to a specific outside object, the mother. Then comes the development of memory traces and thought processes, and, finally, concept formation with verbal symbols.

This is only a bare outline of those meaningful specific events in the child's encounter with his environment that are of central significance in determining the degree of certainty that the adult will have of his continuing integrated and coherent self-identity. Nor do the first 15 to 18 months see the end of the development of the sense of self. We are equally aware of its development through childhood, adolescence, young adulthood, middle years, and old age. There is evidence that all psychological development, including the sense of self, is not the product of the first years of life alone. Spitz indicates that further investigations probably will yield evidence of "organizers" in the later years beyond the three that he has outlined.

At this juncture, we face a great many unanswered questions and questions that have not as yet been clearly formulated. During the remainder of this presentation I will consider some of these questions, in an effort to paint a broader picture of the complexity of the human organism in its relationship to itself and to the world outside. Some of these questions are: (1) In what circumstances does a threat to the loss of one's identity arise? (2) What influences determine the outcome of such a threat? (3) Might the outcome be a favorable one, so that insecurity about one's sense of identity might be regarded as a positive or a creative development in the life of an individual or even a cultural group or social system?

I will not attempt to suggest other specific organizers but instead will indicate events in the early years and in later life that appear to be of critical significance. First, there is the necessary disruption of the early symbiotic relationship between mother and child. This development has a critical effect on the child's sense of his own separate identity. In order to achieve this the child must have that optimal degree of both frustration and loving care from the mother that makes it possible for him to recognize the mother as a separate entity, who now gives, now takes away, and at times frustrates by forcing a delay in the insistent demands for immediate gratification made by her infant child. It is possible for the child to recognize and maintain the mother as a separate entity and consequently himself as separate from her only by having experience when the mother is not there or does not respond immediately. When she does respond, she must be able to calm the angry, frustrated cries of the infant with a relaxed reassurance. She can accomplish this only if she has not waited until the child is having a crying fit or panic with an attendant loss of confidence. Despair or loss of hope occurs in the infant when there is excessive stimulation from frustrated rage. This situation can overwhelm and traumatize the infant's developing ego unless it is neutralized by love from the mother. Neutralized anger acts as a vital building block to the ego and therefore helps to further differentiate between inside and outside, between "me" and "not me."

This differentiation is solidified further by later experiences with toilet training, development of friendships, adolescent gangs, and sexual intimacy. Nevertheless, self-identity is never static or fixed. The roots of the early symbiotic identification with the mother are always present within the adult so that return to this ego state is a frequent occurrence and, for some, an ever present threat. I am referring here not only to severe regression, such as occurs in schizophrenia, but also to the regression that occurs in neurotic or character disorders. In these one can observe residuals of, or regression to, symbiotic attachments to the mother figure that make loving a separate, independent object difficult or impossible. This situation may occur in either sex, but it is considerably more complex in women, whose psychosexual development necessitates a shift from the original love object, the mother, to the father. In women one more often sees identity problems in which confused psychosexual identification is combined with an insecure sense of self-identity. The identity problem in the female is often less conspicuous and less easily recognized than in the male because her symbiotic attachment to the mother can shift to a clear identification with her mother, so that identification and object love are directed to the same person. This may hide the underlying identity conflict, at least until she reaches adolescence, when it becomes more evident. In contrast, the male, in making the shift from symbiosis to identification, must replace symbiosis with object love and make his major identification with his father. The male, therefore, more often fails to make the crucial transition from symbiosis to object love. While his identification with his father may be adequate enough to insure a sense of sexual maleness, he may nevertheless be unable to love a woman as an independent object separate from himself. In this case, his sense of self-identity may be so infused with his mother that it is difficult for him to separate self love from object love.

The process of identification with significant others is not limited to the first few years of life and relationships with the mother or father, although these identifications with parents are necessary in the development of the ego and consequently of the sense of self. Identifications with siblings, relatives, friends, spouses, heroes, and prominent figures in the community play a role in the development of the self. The individual's self-identity is constantly being tested and buffeted by changes in the social group, the cultural traditions, and the family unit. The sense of self is influenced and in part formed by interaction with the members of the immediate family and by the values of the community. The shifts in community and family values act both as a threat and as a catalyst to the integrative and synthetic functions of the individuals ego. When these functions are threatened or defective, the sense of identity suffers. Conversely, when an identity crisis occurs, the ego's synthetic and integrative functions are stimulated and catalyzed to increased efforts to minimize the identity crises and to maximum synthesis in the ego. With this in mind, we may now consider some specific answers to the questions that I have raised.

Erik Erikson has described a series of identity crises in the life history of every individual. Such a crisis is provoked, for example, in the child whose self-esteem is intimately related to the role of being a loving child who satisfies the mother's needs just because he is her baby and who is then confronted with the disconcerting experience of having to be, not a baby, but a "big boy" who is expected to behave in certain situations just like the older siblings or the parents. His identity must therefore confront a shift from "baby is loved" to "big boy is loved" when he does *not* do what used to bring personal pleasure as well as rewarding approval. Thus, to walk, to talk, or to deposit excreta only at certain prescribed times and places must become part of his image of himself. This contradicts his previous image and represents a conflict that is frustrating but is, at the same time, catalytic for his further development. His image, then, must change to being "cute and acceptable" not when he strikes out, or hits, or bites, but when he plays with others peacefully and eventually does "good work in school," thus becoming engaged in productive tasks. This represents a new identity and with it a more creative and productive ego capability. In the same way, in adolescence an identity crisis arises when the previous self-concept of a preadolescent "playboy" whose self-esteem is rooted in close relationships with the same sex must shift to include that which before was forbidden and frowned upon; "the other world of sexual intimacy and closeness" with the opposite sex. This world that he had struggled a few years earlier quite successfully to inhibit and suppress now becomes the expected norm and the proper way he is to handle increased biological sexual urges. Furthermore, he must separate these female creatures from their counterparts, which they resemble so closely (namely their mothers), and from his own mother as well. This shift must include also the meaning of fantasies that he had only a few years earlier been able to suppress and forget in order to conform to the previous expectation of himself as an industrious and studious preadolescent boy in the latency period. Out of this confusion and struggle, he must terminate his shaky adolescent identity, insofar as one exists at all, and replace it with an ego ideal that has its expectation in union with the opposite sex and with the consequent new identity of parenthood. It is such crises that, along with biological and maturational factors, provide stimulus for a new identity and a new self-concept. Later identity crises may occur at the point of career decision, or even in role changes or position changes within the chosen career.

What are some of the road blocks that may stand in the way of a successful, integrated resolution of these epigenetic crises? Let me emphasize that an unsuccessful resolution at any stage does not usually result in a permanent fixation at that level of development, but it does make the next stage more difficult and less successful.

The intrapsychic discontinuities to which I am referring are no doubt most severely aggravated by disruptions of the family unit, first, and, most severely, by the death of a parent or a sibling or spouse and, second, by divorce and marital discord with all of its complications for the growing child. A not uncommon difficulty is the failure of parental achievement of a significant degree of integration and resolution of the parent's own identity that may or may not be associated with marital discord.

One must not underestimate the influence of social changes on the individual sense of self, but I leave the specific study of these phenomena to the sociologists and social psychologists. What I would like to stress is that we must not ignore the existence of a structure—the sense of self—within the ego, whose developmental course is both influenced and formed by cultural and interpersonal influences operating from birth, as well as by certain inherited and innate givens that come to the individual from his collective past.

In addition, there is a continuous dynamic interchange between the intrapsychic structural elements and the social and cultural group norms. For example, when there has been a developmental defect in the sense of identity, the individual turns to the social group to augment or bolster his threatened lack of self. Those whose sense of self is most lacking cling most tightly to group mores and group identity, while those whose life circumstances have been such as to produce a more certain sense of themselves, are more independent of a particular social group; to them the group becomes a valuable experience, but not a necessity. If the former individual, for a variety of possible reasons, is not able to bolster his self-identity by identification with a group possessing a more solid sense of values than his own, he may suffer intense anxiety and unrest. In the face of this, he may return to the symbiotic attachment to a mother or mother figure, or he may be more severely damaged and be able to find solace only in a world of his own fantasy, often devoid of human object meaning. We call this schizophrenia. Even when the individual attempts to bolster his threatened sense of identity in an appropriate group, the "solution" may not always be a happy one. The result may be such a dependent symbiotic attachment to the group that, given a number of such individuals in the same group, there may take place a development of distrust, hostility, and prejudice against other groups or other individuals. This development in group psychology is not surprising when we recognize that the attachment to a group is characterized in the individual by loss of some of his sense of individuality, associated with a lessening of discriminative intellectual and other ego functions. This in turn results in increased credulity and decreased reality testing, which is replaced by stereotyping and overgeneralization. The act of group attachment, therefore, often backfires, with the loss of individual self-esteem that is a regular and consistent consequence of the development of prejudice. The loss of self-esteem results from the outer-directed and self-directed hostility inherent in prejudice. It is not surprising that Bettelheim and Janowitz and others investigating the nature of prejudice find it most frequently to be a concomitant of, and perhaps causally related to, an insufficient sense of identity. From a study of prejudiced groups, it becomes clear that this type of symbiotic group formation provides the soil in which prejudiced attacks on other groups or individuals may flourish.

To summarize the effects on the individual of his dependent symbiotic attachment to a group: First, he gives up a certain modicum of his individuality in order to adjust himself to the mores and values of the group. Second, it is characteristic of group, as well as of mass, psychology that the individual members tend to utilize less individual reality testing and to rely instead on generalizations by the group and on their own stereotypes in place of more careful discriminative judgment. Third, the individual with a threatened sense of identity, in an attempt to substitute the group for his proclivity to return to the original symbiosis, may join others with the same difficulty, and the result is a regression of ego controls and a loosening of previously self-contained impulses, especially hostility, with a consequent increase in prejudice, bigotry, discriminative acts, or even violence. Contagion and the imitation of emotion, which are characteristic features of groups, add impetus to these impulses. Fourth, the results of such feelings and behavior cause the individual to lose even more of his already shaky self-esteem, and his self-identity suffers another blow with a consequent increase in fear, panic, and disequilibrium.

While it is true that prejudice acts for some as a defense against the loss of social identity and identity diffusion, through the vicious cycle outlined above the result is greater loss of identity and self-esteem and an increase in prejudice in an ever-increasing spiral. There are, of course, social controls that can interrupt and slow this process, but thus far we have found no real solution to it.

Coming to the final question raised, I am by no means optimistic that the ego-strengthening and creative effects of the developmental identity crises over the lifetime of any individual will predominate. Certain group experiences, particularly the development of prejudice, may nullify any gains made. Identity crises are an unavoidable part of ego development, and as such play a catalytic role in maturation. These crises can contribute either to mental health or to mental illness, depending upon the nature and effect of the traumatic events experienced by the individual during his lifetime and depending also upon the degree of success achieved in handling each crisis as it arises. The implications for prevention and for possible therapeutic intervention are clear, but since my purpose is to present and discuss the problems of identity, I leave the details of possible solution to those who have that responsibility in our symposium.

PSYCHOLOGICAL ASPECTS OF MENTAL HEALTH

By Walcott H. Beatty, Ph.D.

There are, indeed, a bewildering variety of factors to be studied in understanding mental health during the current period of rapid changes and shifting scenes. It would be well to start by delimiting what I, as a psychologist, feel I can contribute. First, I shall concern myself primarily with preventive aspects of the mental illness problem. Second, with due regard for the importance and multiplicity of factors which contribute to mental malfunctioning, I shall assume that, in essence, learning is the process by which mental functioning takes on form. It is my hope that I can present some ideas about learning which will have implications for the prevention of mental illness.

MENTALLY HEALTHY LEARNING

The theory and research on learning coming from experimental psychologists are proudly neutral. They are seeking general principles which explain why people learned what they learned, regardless of what they learned. This is a commendable and necessary step in the advancement of science. However, all of the questions about "learning for what?" remain unanswered. I would like to propose a less neutral category of learning, which is not independent of empirical tests, but is directed toward a useful or applied outcome. This is a category based upon what we know about learning but including a definition of what the learning is attempting to achieve. It is an attempt to answer the question, what stimuli should be presented and what behaviors should be reinforced. I would like to call this category, mentally healthy learning.

Both from my reading of the literature[1] and from my own experience in research,[2] I am well aware of the many pitfalls in trying to define mental health. I can only say that I think it is better to try, and even flounder, and that I offer my ideas as tentative and, I hope, provocative.

My first "definition" involves the substitution of the words "effective functioning" for the words, "mental health." A person who functions

---

[1]Jahoda, M.: Current Concepts of Positive Mental Health. New York, Basic Books, 1958.

[2]Wilhelms, F. et al.: Teacher Education and Mental Health. *Monograph,* San Francisco State College, 1963.

34

effectively in the world is mentally healthy. Clearly this term is as open to interpretation as is "mental health." Since I take a dim view of the prospect that we can ever reach objective agreement concerning the characteristics of effective functioning, I have chosen the alternative that it must be defined in the eye of the functioner. This does not mean that I think all individuals are equally effective or that there are not extremes of behavior that require society to move in with limiting controls. It means, essentially, that I am accepting the assumption that each individual will be motivated toward the goals which he personally perceives and not necessarily toward the ones which you and I might define.

Such an approach leaves room for wide individual differences in what is mentally healthy behavior or mentally healthy goals. It does not, I think, cut us completely adrift. I think there are meaningful generalizations to be made regarding the learnings which are necessary for effective functioning. The particular activities or behaviors which are employed in augmenting these learnings may vary widely, but the purposes are the same.

In order to describe this further I must make an apparent digression. Within a particular learning theory,[3] a self concept learning theory, it is postulated that an individual in interacting with the world builds a concept of what he is like in the world. At the same time through becoming aware of the expectations of the people around him, and through his identifying with important people in his life, he builds a concept of what he should be like. These two concepts are called the perceived-self-in-the-world and the concept of the adequate self. Since one is a reflection of what he has learned that he is in the world and the other is a picture of what he should be, they are clearly different concepts. It is further postulated that the source of long-term motivation for development is the attempt on the part of the individual to become his adequate self. Since there are discrepancies between the perceived self and the adequate self, a motivational state to learn and close the gap between the two is set up. Within this framework, the individual's definition of effective functioning is becoming like his adequate self. Mentally healthy learning then becomes that learning which helps an individual become more adequate. To give substance to the statement requires that we define the nature of adequacy.

From my research and experience, there seem to be four aspects to adequacy or four nodal points toward which behavior is directed. The individual is striving to become worthy, to become able to cope with the situations he must face, to become able to express himself in satisfying ways, and to become autonomous. There are external criteria for each of

[3]Beatty, W., and Clark, R.: A Self Concept Theory of Learning. San Francisco State College (mimeograph), 1961.

these. Our moral codes and society's status system are used as measures of worth. The school and other agencies set the standards for how well one copes. Being able to express oneself is not considered very important, as indicated by our general disapproval of showing feelings or emotions and our low degree of support of the arts. Autonomy is enshrined as a precious right but is currently being so hemmed in by demands for conformity that individual freedom is becoming little more than a rallying cry. These external criteria tend to be so arbitrary, and in many cases actually inhibiting to healthy development, that they can hardly serve as a guide to either the assessment or fostering of mental health.

When one turns to the internal criteria of an individual, it becomes apparent that, while individuals can try to define these aspects of adequacy, the main component is a feeling. A mature, mentally healthy individual feels worthy, without having to prove it; he feels confident that he can cope with any situation he is likely to meet; he feels the fullness and richness of continually expressing his self; and he has an understanding of and acceptance of himself and the world, which gives him a feeling of choice, a feeling of autonomy.

We have developed some ways of measuring feelings, such as the projective techniques, but measurement in this area is certainly not entirely satisfactory yet. However, we do have some understanding of the kind of processes which seem to produce these feelings.

Becoming Worthy

Interpersonal relations in which the individual is reacted to as though he were important seem to build feelings of worth. Love within a family seems to be the major source of early development of such feelings, and this is built upon by later belongingness in groups in school and by the important people in the child's life showing what might be called "respect" for him as a person. The research of Bowlby,[4] Spitz,[5] and Dennis[6] suggests that a development of this feeling may well be the cornerstone for all later development. Children who don't have a loving relationship during the early years seem to have impaired development in all areas. The Gluecks[7] in their studies of delinquency further support the idea that distorted development

[4]Bowlby, J.: Maternal care and mental health. World Health Association, 1952.

[5]Spitz, R. Anaclitic depression: An inquiry into the genesis of psychiatric conditions in early childhood. Psychoanal. Stud. Child 2: 1946.

[6]Dennis, W. Causes of retardation among institutional children: Iran J. Genetic Psychol. 96: 1960.

[7]Glueck, S., and Glueck, E. Potential juvenile delinquents can be identified: What next? Brit. J. Criminol. 4: 1964.

is the result of early experiences which fail to develop feelings of worth. In purest form the experience is one in which there is communication to the child of unconditional love. You are important and wanted, no matter what you do.

Becoming Able to Cope

The human organism is born with few patterns for coping with the world outside. He must develop his potential and learn patterns which become increasingly complex as he matures. The particular culture and society into which he is born provides a cocoon to protect him while he is very young and a model after which he is to pattern his behavior. Not only are the cultural patterns available, but society provides agencies to assure that the growing individual will assimilate and accommodate to the pattern. Thus the family initially and then other agencies, such as the church and school, work actively to induce appropriate patterns of behavior in the child. The role of these agencies is an important and necessary one, and the processes which go on in the family and the school are undoubtedly the key ones in preventive mental health.

The fact that the school is seen primarily as an agency for helping people learn to cope endangers its role as a mental health agency. In my view, the present pressure to return to the fundamentals, to reinstate strict subject matter, and to increase homework is a serious threat to healthy growth and development. It is true that the child needs, and is motivated, to learn to cope, but he must also learn to become worthy, able to express himself, and become autonomous. He must also learn to cope with many things which the school is not teaching in the areas of human relations skills, ways to use leisure time, how to respond creatively, etc. To illustrate my point, possibly the things taught in school represent 20 per cent of what a person needs to learn to be an effective adult, and yet it is demanding close to 60 per cent of his time.

Another problem which arises with agencies helping people become able to cope is closely related to this last point. Because families, schools, churches, and other groups tend to concentrate rather narrowly on only certain knowledge and skills necessary to coping, they find the children often unmotivated to acquire these tools. They are motivated to learn other things which are seen as outside the scope of the particular agency and are therefore disapproved of by the agency. In order to control these unwanted motivations and stimulate motivation in the approved areas, these agencies often manipulate the child's motivation to become worthy. In the family you won't be loved if you don't learn what you are told. In school you won't be an "A" student unless you conform. This confusion of worth with coping ability can cause serious disturbances. Theoretically the two are related but separate. In actuality it is probably not possible to keep them completely separate, but we should look for ways of tapping the motivation to learn to cope—ways in which the ability to cope is not confused with worthiness. The child should be respected as a valuable human whether or not he is learning what someone wants him to learn. I will come back to this matter of how we can draw on a child's motivation in a few minutes.

Expressing

Not all behavior serves the purpose of coping with the world. Some behavior is what we might call expressive. By our very nature we respond to aspects of the world such as color, form, sound, and rhythm. These are satisfying and enriching experiences, and we are motivated to learn how to express these aspects of ourselves. Not only is this expression satisfying, but through our own developing awareness of such feelings we can learn about ourselves and then use our cognitive skills to behave more effectively.

One special case of expressing is particularly important to mental health. This is the expressing of feelings which arise in interpersonal relationships, especially negative ones. Our culture does not approve of overt expression of feelings and emotions, and yet these are human and need satisfying outlets. There is reason to believe that if people were provided with means for expressing feelings or could learn how to do it in nondestructive ways that there would be less buildup to strong or violent emotions which are almost invariably destructive. It should be possible, in other places than a therapist's office, to be able to say, "I'm beginning to feel angry," or "I feel hurt," or "I'm bored," without it being seen as threatening to others. If we do not learn to recognize and accept these feelings in our selves then we tend to project blame on others and say instead, "You are irritating" or "You are hurtful" or "You are boring." This compounds the feeling problem, and when it is done by adults to children it is damaging to their feelings of worth. Agencies working with children must discover how they can help children express themselves in constructive ways.

Autonomy

As the child begins to feel he has worth, and that he can cope with the world and express himself, he develops feelings of autonomy. The essential nature of autonomy is the feeling that one can make a choice. It is clear that this can be fostered by giving individuals increasing responsibility and opportunities for making choices. We have many fears about this. We distrust a growing child's ability to make choices. We are often afraid that he will make a mistake, when actually there are many situations in which making a mistake provides an excellent learning opportunity. It usually seems less dangerous and easier to make the choices for the child. It seems to me that the pressures towards conformity and the elimination of choice-making have reached the point where it is unlikely that most children can really actualize some of their potential and become mature, responsible people.

Striving for Adequacy

The typical activities of a child in the process of striving for adequacy change over time as his concept of adequacy develops. Some generalizations can be made about the activities which are typical at various ages. For example, in striving to become worthy the preschool child must learn to relate emotionally to adults and siblings. He imitates their behavior and learns the things which please them and lead them to include him in their activities. When he comes to school he must extend this relationship to the teacher and to his classmates and build his behaviors in ways which are appropriate to his sex role. As he moves into adolescence the activities concern testing and accepting his body, developing further an appropriate sex role, and learning to relate to members of the opposite sex. Throughout all of this he will be learning and using ways of getting feedback as to whether or not he is perceived as worthy. The earliest and simplest ways to get such feedback is through attention-getting behavior. Many children never learn more mature or effective ways than this and are still attention-getters as adults. Others get such feedback through finding belongingness in groups and deepening personal relationships with various individuals.

At the preschool age becoming more able to cope includes learning bladder and bowel control, learning to walk and talk, to eat appropriately, and the learning of simple skills and concepts. In school the child must learn more advanced skills such as reading and writing and expanded concepts about the world and the rules which govern individual and group behavior. All of these continue to grow in adolescence along with ideas of economic independence, vocational competence, and social skills.

The area of becoming adequate in expressing the self is one which, as I have indicated, is most neglected, not only in school but in the family and in society generally. In preschool days it develops fairly naturally through play activities and general exploration of what the world feels, tastes, smells, sounds, and looks like. In the early years in school, opportunities for using art media, hearing music, and talking in "show-and-tell" periods foster this development. From about nine or ten years of age it is left pretty much to chance and is, in many ways, discouraged. Some elective courses such as art, band, drama, and athletics provide learning opportunities for the expressive aspect of adolescents, but this does not help too many. The rest develop it as well as they can through the adolescent peer group which condones swearing, risk taking, jazz, etc.

As each of these three areas develop so that the child feels more worthy, more able to cope, and more able to express, there is a growing awareness of alternatives and choices. As the child explores these successfully he gains in the feeling of autonomy. In preschool days as he learns to walk and talk and has greater freedom to move around he tries out his body in various ways and strives for greater personal independence from adults. In school his personal independence increases, and he begins to develop some values and social attitudes. In adolescence he works on emotional independence of adults, develops more socially responsible behavior, and explores the personal values he wants to live by.

Psychological maturity and mental health are the full development of these feelings of adequacy. The individual comes gradually to feel worthy, without the need to prove it; he has confidence that he can cope with life situations; he is able to express and find gratification for the rich complexity of his self; and he accepts this self and feels free to make choices which genuinely reflect his integrated feeling-thinking processes.

IMPLICATIONS

It should be pointed out that one idea which is implicit throughout all of the foregoing discussion is that motivation is completely internal. We may offer incentives or rewards to influence behavior, but their effectiveness is dependent upon whether or not the child is motivated to acquire the incentive or achieve the reward. There are various ways in which we can manipulate his motivation so that he may do things which seem irrelevant to him in order to achieve other ends. I have already given one example of this while discussing coping. We use the motivation to become worthy as the means to coerce him to learn some skill or knowledge by threatening to find him unworthy if he refuses. I believe that this tends to distort healthy development and keep the individual immature and dependent.

Any learning which really helps an individual relate effectively to the world will be worked on eagerly by that individual. If the individual responds negatively or resists the learning he is telling us that he sees it as irrelevant to his adequacy. There may be many reasons for this. It may be genuinely irrelevant. At one time we believed that the learning of Latin was relevant for all high school students. Many many students were telling us, in various ways, that it was irrelevant long before the school agreed. Another reason for resistance to learning is that the timing may be wrong. Twelve-year-old boys generally resist learning to dance but may be eager to learn a few years later.

A much more serious problem is that some children develop very impoverished concepts of adequacy. Inconsistent or nonexistent expectations for how they should develop or the existence of unhealthy models with whom they identify start them off in life with disorganized or distorted pictures of adequacy. The so-called disadvantaged children are disadvantaged in just this way. Their concepts of adequacy are such that learning in school and the expectations of society seem to a large degree to be irrelevant, and hence they are unmotivated to learn these things.

There is an implication in all this. As I see it, it means that anyone working with children, regardless of whether or not the earlier learning of the children has been mentally healthy, will be fostering mental health if he sees himself as a facilitator of an ongoing process which cannot be directly controlled. We can intimidate and coerce children and try to manipulate their motivation, but this will either be unsuccessful, or worse, it will disrupt mentally healthy development.

Instead, to the extent that we can, we will always treat the child as though he is important and worthy. We will specifically avoid ridicule, sarcasm, and punishment. It is probably also unnecessary to use praise. Whenever it is used there is always the implication that next time the work may not be praiseworthy. Just the interest we have in the child and an ever-ready offer to help will communicate to him that he is worthy.

The specific help we give may be some knowledge or skill that will enable him to cope better, but it will be given because in some way he was asking for it and not because we think it is good for him. A recent book, *Teacher* by Sylvia-Ashton-Warner,[8] gives a fascinating example of how this can be done. With a method she calls "organic reading" she tries to discover the words which have the most meaning or emotional loading for the child. When she discovers one she prints it in large letters on a card and gives it to the child. These cards lead to what she calls "one look" learning. As the days go by the teacher keeps adding words as the child reveals them. Many words which are not learned are removed as not being personally meaningful enough to be important at this stage. The reading vocabulary which is built in this way is a deeply meaningful one which makes reading a tremendously important activity.

We will encourage the child to use all media of expression and to find those which have meaning to him. In particular we will encourage the expression of feelings and encourage him to evaluate what they mean and how he can express them in ways which do not do damage either to himself or to other people.

---

[8]Ashton-Warner, Sylvia: Teacher. New York, Simon & Shuster, 1963.

Finally, we will offer opportunities for choices; we will let him make mistakes if they will not be damaging to him, and help him evaluate what happened and why, and how he could avoid the mistake another time. We will encourage him to take responsibility as he is able to.

We can foster mentally healthy development if the learning processes allow the child to relate more effectively to the world as he perceives it.

In this paper I have suggested the need for a concept called mentally healthy learning. I have defined this as processes that help the child feel worthy, able to cope with the world, able to express his self, and become increasingly autonomous. I am probably more aware than the reader of the inadequacies of the formulation. It is still too vague and leaves many questions unanswered. It is an attempt to develop some thinking on what I consider to be one of the vital problems of preventive mental health. I hope it stimulates some of you to carry work forward on the problem.

SOCIOLOGICAL ASPECTS OF MENTAL WELL-BEING

By RALPH LANE, JR., PH.D.

My purpose is to review the major traditions in sociology, as they relate to the concept of mental well-being. My intent is to point out what consequences these traditions, actually two major ones, have in terms of a view of mental health or, of course, ill-health or deviation. For, short of indulging ourselves in some kind of utopian notion of the *good society*, it appears to me that the manner in which we approach the question of the optimum conditions for mental well-being (particularly since these are understood to be conditions of social structure and, therefore, subject to rational or not-so-rational planning)˙ has implications which go well beyond the realm of the mere academic.

One important tradition has focused on the process of socialization, since the manner in which the individual is introduced into the roles, or the total social role, which he or she will play is a crucial consideration in deciding whether or not there is a possibility of mental well-being among the members of a society. This concern has been preempted to a large extent by those who have come under the influence of Freud and all the Schools stemming from his influence. These would include myriad psychiatrists, psychologists, such luminary social psychologists as G. H. Mead, Cooley, Jean Piaget, and, somewhat more recently, Fromm, Horney, and Arnold Green, as well as the anthropologists who have shared the orientation of Margaret Mead and Ruth Benedict. To some extent I am doing all of them a grave injustice by putting them in a category of common concern, but indeed they do have a like interest with the socialization process in general and role continuities and discontinuities in particular. This has been a very fruitful concern not only for the light it sheds on the socialization process —that is, the introduction of the new member into the society—but also because it can point up the problematic aspect of other points of status/role transition in the life cycle. Thus, much of the work in this tradition has sharpened our understanding of the transition from an adulthood full of meaning, generally in terms of career for the male and of nuclear-family intensity for the woman, to the post-65 period which is seen as a kind of limbo with regard to both role and corresponding status. Suicide, for example, correlates very highly with this particular transition, as my own previous research here in San Francisco has indicated. Similarly, of course, the rolelessness of adolescence, to return to an earlier stage in the life cycle,

43

helps us in part to understand something about the nature of juvenile delinquency and, presumably, about the juvenile delinquent as an individual with problems of mental health.

Although this has obviously been an important approach, an exclusive focus in this area may distract attention from what I, as well as some of my sociological colleagues, think is a largely neglected but vitally important concern which, we will see, has rather deeper ideological implication. (In addition, we are not too sure that the socialization approach is exclusively that of sociologists even if we have managed to muscle in, as has been suggested by Professor Maas' paper.) The concern with the socialization process and with role continuities in general may never thrust us up against the question of the kind of society within which, one is hopeful, individuals can be integrated. It is this more general consideration of the total society which I think bears some examination.

The anthropological literature and some of the sociological monographs which treat of class differentials, although concerned, as in the first approach, with the socialization process, do come to terms with the end product—that is, the integrated individual—and with the quality of the culture into which this individual has been successful in integrating. But, it appears to me, especially in the anthropological writings, the treatment is heavily value laden, characterized by a certain amount of romantic nostalgia. As a flagrant example, see Benedict's treatment of the Apollonian character of the Zuni as opposed to the Dionysianism of the Kwakiutl. The former she diagnoses as representing a model of equilibrium and the latter as having wide streaks of paranoia.

To a great extent American sociology, the ideological impetus for which derives from a rural bias, has also been value laden. It has tended, for example, to see the flux and conflict of the urban milieu as dysfunctional both from the viewpoint of societal or system maintenance and of the potential integration of the personality. Deviant behavior, therefore, whether viewed sociologistically, as in this second tradition, as a product of social disorganization (or the more modern formulation, *anomie*) or psychologistically, as in the first tradition discussed, as a product of inadequacies in the socialization process, is seen to threaten the well-being, the on goingness, so to speak, of the society. This, it appears to me, has led us to, or at least reinforced, a negative evaluation of heterogeneity. It has resulted in a preference for a homogeneity which at best borders on the mediocre.

At this point I would like to dissociate myself from a kind of warmed-over laissez-faire competitiveness. This "survival of the fittest" ideology may actually be indifferent to the validity of variant positions and may, in fact, have resulted in compulsive conformity, since all are encouraged to model themselves after the victor. Nor am I advancing a Nietzschean or Ayn Rand position which puts a literal premium on Polonius' admonition, "To thine own self be true." Rather, I am speaking of the value, from the viewpoint of mental health, that tension or conflict may have as a continuous, ongoing process in the society.

In part, of course, this kind of position is dilemmic, since we recognize that there is a critical point beyond which tension or conflict is dysfunctional and ultimately leads to chaos or anarchy. But, at the same time, it appears that this may be a welcome antidote to the undue stress put on that side of the equation which, as I have indicated, always evaluates deviance in the negative frame of reference. As a growing social psychological literature of disenchantment attests, this one-sided emphasis has resulted in our institutions having become geared to the normal curve. We are, therefore, unable to engender any real creativity.

This institutional homogeneity, or pressure in that direction, has most likely been intensified by such competitive processes as the arms race with the Soviet Union. At the same time, however, there seems to have arisen, probably quite independently, a fear of pluralism. This is, indeed, the point at which there is the deepest ideological implication. When we speak of integration of minority groups into the mainstream of life in our society, as a desirable goal, we may very well mean that we cannot tolerate the differences which their past or present ways of life represent. The phrase *cultural deprivation,* for example, may simply be a liberal euphemism for disapproval since, in one sense, in the way that anthropologists use the word "culture," one cannot really be culturally deprived. Or, at least, groups cannot be spoken of as lacking cultures. Indeed, as is well known, they do have subcultures if they have minority status in a wider society, and it is precisely the norms of these subcultures which run counter to those of the dominant majority. I would suggest, in this regard, that the kind of value discrepancies which William Madsen has revealed in his study *Mexican-Americans of South Texas* is very much to the point.

If I may refer to an area very close to home, to San Francisco, in which conceptions of what is the *good society* and, by reflection, what is good for the mental well-being of the individual may be based on this unwillingness to admit the viability of pluralism, I would like to ask you to consider what kinds of goals we have in mind when we talk about urban renewal. If we mean something which is basically of a hygienic middle-class character, then it seems to me that we are, in effect, revealing our own anxieties about the human condition. We have, all too unwittingly, failed to accept what Paul Tillich refers to as the *existential anxiety* of that condition, and we have failed to see the fruitfulness of what Martin Luther King has called the *creative tension* of our times.

As a final word, I would simply share with Professor Maas his concern for the homeostatic nature of the mental health movement unless it is able and willing to question its own goals.

THE EFFECTS OF COMMUNITY CHANGE—
A PANEL

Editor's Note:

In the following panel presentation and discussion, two sociologists, an economist and a psychiatrist team up to handle the issues involved in community change. In this exchange, each panel member presents some aspects of community change, after which the panel deals with questions from the participating audience. Alfred Auerback reacts to the change occurring in the role and stance of psychiatry and psychiatrists as a result of changes in basic attitudes toward the ubiquitous problem of mental illness. Egon Bittner raises the question of the changing function of *work* in our society as it relates to mental health. John Condliffe raises the questions of the effects of poverty, unemployment, the industrial revolution, automation, and social security on mental health. Nathan Glazer is concerned with the effects of urban renewal, defense cutbacks, and changes in the racial composition of neighborhoods.

PANEL PRESENTATION

ALFRED AUERBACK, M.D., *Chairman*
EGON BITTNER, Ph.D., JOHN CONDLIFFE, D.Sc., NATHAN GLAZER, Ph.D.

ALFRED AUERBACK, M.D.

Psychiatry from the beginning has concerned itself with the mental health of the individual, and up to the present time most psychiatrists are trained in the technique of a one-to-one relationship. However, it has become increasingly evident that the patient does not exist in a vacuum: he belongs to a family, lives in a community, usually holds a job, and often belongs to a church and other social groups. As a consequence, psychiatry has been forced to pay more attention to family relationships and to the environmental pressures involved in the patient's life. We see the development of two new concepts in psychiatry—social psychiatry and community psychiatry. Social psychiatry is concerned with people in numbers, studying social and environmental factors that affect people in their relationships. Many studies have been conducted regarding the way the community and its inhabitants are integrated. Perhaps the best known of these is the Midtown Manhattan Project, although there have been a number of other excellent sociological or social psychiatric studies. In these studies, an attempt is made to ascertain the extent of psychiatric illness in a sample population, considering the ethnic and religious origins of the individuals, sex and age distribution, educational levels, the nature of the psychiatric illness, and the extent to which these people have sought psychiatric help. An effort is made to find the different types of life experience which might have a relationship to mental disorder including the age of the individual, his physical health, and socioeconomic status, the occurrence of death in the family, or breakup of the home and the nature of the home relationships. In addition, to ascertaining the extent of psychotic and neurotic illness and psychosomatic disorder in the community we now realize that psychopathology can show itself in other ways—the criminal, the delinquent, the school dropout, the person who has employment problems, the people who get divorced, and the people who use alcohol excessively. These are all measures of the mental health of the community.

In the field of community mental health, we are trying to provide a broad spectrum of comprehensive mental health services for the people in the community in need of help using inpatient and outpatient services, day care, emergency services, consultative and educational programs, diagnostic and rehabilitation services, vocational training, after care, halfway houses, research and evaluation. There are radical changes going on within the community itself which have a tremendous impact upon the individual. One of these is the accelerated drift of people from the country to the city so that our cities are merging into large megalopoleis. There is increasing racial tension associated with the problems of integration. Urban renewal means mass dislocation for large numbers of individuals. Work patterns change as the computer replaces the individual. Blue collar jobs become fewer, meaning less job opportunities for the unskilled or the poorly educated. Whole industries run the risk of becoming obsolete overnight. Superimposed on this are other problems—shadows of the atomic bomb, the breakup of long-established empires and the emergence of nations with strong nationalistic tendencies, the revolutionary doctrine of communism on one hand and the radical philosophy of the so-called "right wing" at the other extreme, the uncertainties of our economic system with recurrent episodes of boom, recession, even depression. Above all of this hangs the ever-present threat of that periodic insanity called war. Other problems include the increase in pollution of our air and our water, the decrease of timber and mineral resources, and in some countries shortages of food. These are some of the changes going on in our world at the present time. I am sure that you will agree that each of these in its own way leaves its imprint upon the individual and upon society. Some 300 years ago John Donne wrote "No man is an island, entire of itself." We are all of us part of a community, whether a town or a city in a larger geographical area called a state, in a larger area called a country, in a world which at one time seemed very large, but which now has shrunk in size. Jet travel and the rocket have brought us very close together, and yet this world is a very small satellite of a minor star in a minor galaxy in a myriad of galaxies in a gigantic expanse of space that we are now beginning to explore through the miracle of space travel. This is our community. Obviously, during the next hour we cannot hope to touch on the many subjects which may have some impact on the individual and his mental health. Our discussion will confine itself to changes going on in our cities and in the communities in which we live, assessing their import and their impact upon the individual and the community.

EGON BITTNER, PH.D.

I should like to start by making a general observation about this conference. As we are trying to understand and describe the relationship between community change and mental health, we are obliged to pretend that we are viewing this relationship, as it were, from the outside. This conceit alleges that our deliberations are not a part of what we are talking about. A moment of reflection reveals, however, that talking about mental health, as we do now, is a relatively recent phenomenon. Whatever part madness and sanity have played in the course of history, the problem of mental hygiene achieved a position of unprecedented salience only in our time. Thus we had better keep in mind that this conference is itself part of the changing community and that, in a larger sense, our talk is part of what we are talking about.

In my remaining remarks I attempt to relate some statements made by Dr. Brockbank to some statements made by Mr. Loban, in his subsequent paper. Dr. Brockbank, as you will recall, presented a psychoanalytic version of the problem of identity and its transformations. Among others he emphasized that while identity formation is usually associated with childhood and adolescence, it is wrong to assume that the process terminates in these stages of growth. Rather, the sense of identity remains viable and monitored from the outside throughout human life. The idea that self-conception or sense of identity are permanently responsive to external influences has a long history in social psychology and sociology. To express this idea Charles Horton Cooley coined the phrase "the looking glass self." The apt metaphor suggests that what a person knows, and how he feels, about himself is an image reflected in the responses of others to him. George Herbert Mead, a contemporary and friend of Cooley, suggested that the "Self" is only partly dependent on the contingent responses of actual other persons and that beyond that it is responsive to "the generalized Other." That is, over and above the formative influence of real persons, and even within these relationships, there functions the formative influence of the *moral order*. This difficult concept, the moral order, refers to the locus of all those considerations in terms of which others judge us, we judge others, and, most importantly, we judge ourselves. This, then, is the ultimate "looking glass," the forming and trans-forming medium of our self-image and the permanent monitor of our identity. Only with reference to it are we, in an experiential sense, ourselves.

Now to turn to some points made by Mr. Loban. As you will see, Mr. Loban urges that the full rehabilitation of former patients of mental hospitals requires that they be provided with work opportunities. In part this demand is related to the fact that in our society gainful employment is the normal way of insuring a minimally adequate standard of living. More important, however, is the consideration that in our society working is not only the prevailing way of making a living but also part of decency. That is, through working a person obtains his wherewithal but also maintains integrity, autonomy, and self-respect. To put it in other words, for us work has the significance of a normal obligation, aside from the fact of it being a practical necessity. This, I take it, is the ultimate justification of Mr. Loban's plea for jobs for former mental patients, that having work will strengthen their sense of personal significance and value. This is so because the duty to work, as an element of the moral order in which we live, is a consideration in terms of which we judge ourselves.

I should like to take a few moments to expand on the idea of work as an element of the moral order and a refractor of the self-image. Not only is it common for us to associate moral value with work, but in the hierarchy of our values there are scarcely any that exceed its importance. It seems perfectly natural for us to question the character of any person who systematically and without legitimate excuse avoids work. Work appears to have a virtually unqualified prior claim on our time. We regard it as proper to organize all other interests and activities around our work obligations. Perhaps I can best illustrate the paramount position of work in the schema of things if I call to your attention that when we confront some obligation that we wish to avoid—let us say that we would rather not go to the family Thanksgiving dinner or to some church service or we would like to avoid jury duty—what better excuse could we mobilize than a conflicting work obligation? Consider also how the importance of work is reflected in common speech. A man's vocation is what he does for a living, a man's profession is what he does for a living, and only the irresolute or the irascible would dare to say, when asked of their occupation, that they are presently occupied by being in love, or something like that. Think of our vocabulary of virtues—for example, thrift, economy, prudence, industry, perseverance, ambition, achievement, realism, practicality, and so on— and you will readily see how much of it is tied to work activities. To say the least, for us work is certainly the prime testing ground of a person's character. Would it not therefore be reasonable to assume that the frustrations arising from being denied access to work must either be destructive to a strong sense of identity or must lead to a rebellious denial of the relevance of the moral order of which work is a part?

It is, however, a well-known fact that work is hard to come by. It is hard to come by not only for the mentally and physically handicapped but also for the too young and the too old, for those not sufficiently educated, for the members of some ethnic groups, and for many other groups. It is also a well-known fact, of course, that the federal government and other governmental agencies have recently made a considerable effort to expand work opportunities and to prepare people for them. The hope which inspires all these efforts, and I consider Mr. Loban's statement part of this, is that a growing economy will be able to accommodate all available labor resources. Because of its short-term objectives the program deserves unqualified and strong support. With reference to long-run objectives, however, it appears to have a decidedly lopsided character. The economy is being prodded less to increase its output than to increase its capacity to absorb resources. Though some of us can see the need for many things that are not produced now, the fact is that nothing short of a radical transformation of the structure of our economy could produce a state of affairs in which more labor would be genuinely needed. Quite the contrary, the development of industrial technology portends a future in which what most of us could conceivably do will be done more economically without our participation. In this sense, at least, work as an intrinsically important and intrinsically necessary activity is rapidly disappearing. As this is coming to pass it becomes increasingly difficult for large masses of people to find in work a sense of a socially sanctioned identity, and, therefore, to insist that men must find in work the central value of their lives borders on hypocrisy.

I should like to conclude by recommending for your consideration that the sustained emphasis on the moral value of work and the progressive disappearance of satisfying lines of work for large masses of people, who either cannot find work at all or who when working are doomed to meaningless and degrading tasks, presents a profound cultural dilemma and produces an accompanying, widespread identity crisis. There is a peculiar irony in the fact that work defined as a primordial human calling has produced the very civilization in which it is becoming obsolescent. The time has come, it seems to me, for all of us to search the horizon of human possibilities for some other calling for man.

John B. Condliffe, D.Sc.

I don't know how to define mental health or the lack of it. I'm reminded that I once took a visitor to see Robinson Jeffers at Carmel. My friend had been successful in finding an English poet who had dropped out of circulation for many years—found him incredibly enough in a place called Minerva, Ohio. He told us this story and at the end of it he said, "You know, Mr. Jeffers, I was prepared for almost anything except to find that the atomic age had driven him out of his mind." I shall not forget in a hurry the reply from Robinson Jeffers, sitting quietly by that famous fireside. "What do you mean? Who's out of his mind?"

If I knew how to define mental illness, I wouldn't know how to begin to explore its incidence by locality, by income classes, by age and sex, by religion, national and racial groups, or over time, or as affected by external influences. We economists are used to working with defective statistics, but the statistics of mental health would, I think, test us.

All of us here are social students—we think that environmental conditions have some influence on personality. I quote the most famous economist of my day who might have been writing about the present time instead of three quarters of a century ago, "Those who have been called the residuum of our large towns have little opportunity for friendship, they know nothing of the decencies and the quiet and very little even of the unity of family life, and religion often fails to reach them. No doubt their physical, mental and moral ill health is partly due to other causes than poverty, but poverty is the chief cause."

None of us, I suppose, have any doubt that poverty, unemployment, malnutrition, bad housing, and family anxiety erode the personality and have effects beyond the individual. But we simply have no statistical or scientific data to know whether poverty is the chief cause of mental ill health. Nor can we tell whether the steps that we have taken to cope with these social problems have done very much to help.

I suppose the moderator will find psychiatric meaning in the fact that I go back to my origins, but let me quote you a verse that was written by the chief planner of social reform in New Zealand when New Zealand was a pioneer in this field. The man who was responsible for the first social security act in 1893 was also a poet. He wrote a verse which expressed his ideals for New Zealand:

> Not multitudes starving and striving,
> Not bondsmen of misery's dearth;
> But builders with patience contriving
> A kindlier realm upon earth.
> Where pity old age shall environ,
> Where the young start abreast in their race,
> Nor shall Fate with a gauntlet of iron
> Smite poverty's face.

This was an ambitious social program launched three quarters of a century ago. New Zealand has achieved most of it, yet the moderator has just told us that the New Zealanders are quite unhappy people. Social security has not taken away the problem of mental ill health.

I am not sure how far the outside pressures that impinge on an individual are the cause of mental disturbance. The biochemists may yet find some predisposing physical cause. I hope they will. It would be much easier to modify the chemistry of one human being than it would be to change the whole human race and its impact on that human being.

Population increases rapidly, especially in California. More people live in a city environment; there is less employment in manual and purely clerical labor: machines take over the heavy and also the purely routine work. The handling and management of these machines will require different attitudes. There will be less blue collar and more white collar jobs requiring greater literacy and more intensive training. Much of the new work will be demanding and require intense mental concentration. The computer must be fed with data that is broken down in logical sequence. If the sequence is not logical the machine will spit it out. The pressures on management to control the flow of data and to avoid being swamped by it will call for severe intellectual discipline.

All this one can say—but this is not a new story. It is a very old story. If one looks at the economic history of any country, one will find that economists have been arguing about the effects of machinery upon the working people, at least since the industrial revolution. There was a tremendous controversy concerning the effects of machines from the time when steam power was first used and the factory system developed. The Luddites went around smashing machines. We have some would-be Luddites now. Old jobs always disappear and new jobs take their place. We have more people employed in the United States than we have ever had and most of them employed at better and more rewarding jobs.

It is true that when the first novelty wears off, mechanical work tends to become monotonous. This has been known for a long time. It is also true that we have massive social problems to face. To me, and I suppose to most of us here, this seems an exciting prospect, offering to our children and our grandchildren the chance to build a richer civilization than the world has ever known. But perhaps we aren't typical. There are many people who feel themselves incapable of understanding this new world that is coming into being or adjusting to it, let alone controlling it.

We shall have to take care of many of these people. We need more institutional arrangements. The only economic dictum I am going to assert is that we can surely afford them. In fact we cannot afford not to take care of those overtaken by calamity beyond their individual control. For the young we shall need not only more schools but more highly trained specialists to devise ways of handling the disturbed, the delinquent, and the inadequately motivated—and this we can afford too.

I suppose the most difficult problem is the problem of transitory pressure upon the individual. We no longer have much need for laborers to dig ditches, build railroads, sweep streets, operate elevators, or unload ships. Soon we may be able to dispose of typists, telephone operators, and filing clerks. Some of those being displaced can be retrained to handle the machines that take over their jobs, but many will have to find other jobs within their capacities and skills. We may have to invent things for them to do.

But I don't know, and I doubt if anybody knows, how all this mechanization is going to affect mental health. It will certainly put some people over the edge of anxiety into different kinds of fantasy. But whether this will be a greater rather than a lesser proportion of the total population, I, for one, could not be sure. I should doubt it.

The number of failures will obviously depend on our ability to detect early symptoms and to devise remedial methods to turn their frustration into more rewarding and creative channels. But first we must know more of the nature, the extent, the distribution, and the causes of mental illness. There is no area of scientific research more important and more neglected than this is to the well-being of future generations. We are spending this year, in this country, about 20 billion dollars on scientific research and development. Very little of it is being spent on these human problems. It seems to me that it is time we remember that "the proper study of mankind is man."

NATHAN GLAZER, PH.D.

I suppose I am as floored as Dr. Condliffe was by the notion of mental health and what its relationship might be to a changing community. One famous study attempted to determine whether there has been more mental disorder as life has gotten more complicated. We assume life has gotten more complicated as social change has become more rapid. The main conclusion of this study is that as far back as you can measure mental disorder there has always seemed to be just about the same amount in the United States. But other studies suggest that whatever the stability in the incidence of mental disorder over the past 150 years, it is certainly worse if you are worse off in obvious ways, such as poorer, and having more immediate practical troubles. Whether we use measures of treatment by class and by income . . . or measures of incidence, as in the Mid-town Study Dr. Auerback referred to, it is much worse if you're poor. Another thing these studies conclude is that change is a strain—migration, movement, being required to do something different. Again, I am reminded of Dr. Condliffe's remarks on how work gets boring no matter how interesting it is, how the President probably gets bored in the seventh year of his eight-year term and is happy enough to leave. That seems like a challenging enough job. Nevertheless, most people don't seem to have the resources to meet permanent and continuous challenge.

I have in mind and want to speak about three kinds of changes that are taking place in our communities, and all of them I assume are affecting mental health. All of them are putting more pressure on people. All of them in some sense represent some progress, and all of them raise the problem of how we balance the kinds of changes that take place in our society to create a sound social setting—something which makes people happy or prevents them from becoming unhappy. The three changes I am thinking about are the changes produced by urban renewal, that is by a planned effort to improve the city; the economic impact of such things as cutting off defense contracts and so on; and changes in the racial composition of neighborhoods. I think if we look at them from the point of view of mental health we will probably come to the conclusion that all of them are a threat to a lot of people.

The first change is the urban renewal change—the sort of thing that will happen in the Western Addition section of the Fillmore section of San Francisco, in which, for the improvement of the community and on the advice of certain analysts, it will be necessary to remove large numbers of people who occupy poor housing and low priced housing and replace them with people who can pay for more housing. This will be necessary to maintain the middle class or the high tax-paying element in larger measure in the city. It will be necessary to strengthen the tax base of the city; some people think it is also necessary to improve the looks of the city and so on. Now as a matter of fact, this is one of the types of change around which there is a good deal of social research. I have in mind particularly the very large, by social research standards, study of the impact of renewal project on the mental health of people who were moved out of an area of Boston, the west end of Boston—this was a largely Italian section. I think you are familiar enough with the general pattern of old neighborhoods to have a sense of what happens to them. Among those moved are old people who have lived there a long time and have friends and a church and business people with whom they speak. The businessmen have been there a long time. And most of them, by the way, are rather unproductive in terms of any measures you can provide. The old people don't fill jobs that are necessary to the city. They are on relief or on a pension. The businessmen just barely keep alive, and if anyone were to teach them anything about a balance sheet it would be clear that they should go bankrupt twice a year but they don't—their children send in 30 dollars a month. The old man is happier running the uneconomic grocery store or something. And then there are the other elements. The old probably though suffer the most, as these studies show, because they are cut off from a lot of contact. Urban renewal is thus a cause of change and strain, and we ask the question, how are we going to take this into account when we make decisions on a change about which most people feel positive, that is a change from old buildings to new buildings? How are we going to estimate the cost of that change against the benefits? That's not easy.

Let me go on to another and perhaps even harder problem. The defense situation—the defense contracts. Here is a situation in which everyone agrees the defense budget ought to be lower; no one could imagine that it is useful to continue to produce more plutonium. Yet when any reduction is involved, the threat to people is so great that universally anyone locally involved—Democrat, Republican, mayors, reactionaries, John Birchers and leftwing Democrats all agree, not here, and it should not be done. Now one can say, of course, that this should be related to other kinds of changes, changes which relieve the impact of lowering of defense expenditures and give people new jobs. But this isn't easy. Perhaps, when 500 million dollars is being cut in the defense budget, with good political leadership we can get it appropriated for other useful purposes in the community. But it is also true that if you are working on a ship it is not necessarily true that you can go out counseling dropouts, if that is what we are going to spend the new money on. Or, if we look at a situation such as the proposals for the study for Appalachia. Once again you have this question: do you stop a change in the community? Do you say, nobody wants to build factories there; fine let it go; let everybody move and we will help them out? But even if we do, they have houses; they have friends; this is the place they have always lived. Maybe they are coal miners and the notion of becoming a grocery clerk or whatever else might be in demand in the big city may not be terribly attractive to them. Once again there is a dilemma—do you maintain things, do you maintain operations, do you put in factories that are uneconomic in terms of some measures in order to reduce some other kind of costs, mental health costs, strains on people? Then, at the same time, challenge is rewarding. How much do you challenge or do you give everyone a guarantee? In an urban renewal area do you give them a guarantee they can live there forever? Do you give a guarantee in Appalachia that they can live there forever and that the government will not only see that they don't starve, but make sure that they have work so that then you can feel psychologically healthier than if they were simply on a dole?

My last point raises even more difficult questions, because if you want to vote against change on the first one, or the second one, I wonder how you want to vote on the third—racial transition. If one studies our communities in this country quite honestly, one finds that they have been melting pots in many ways, but any given neighborhood in any given town is not so much of a melting pot. Any given school is not so much of a melting pot. I often think cynically the reason the American common school was so great was because fortunately it was occupied only by white

Protestants, and consequently they weren't troubled by the Jews who were troubled by the Christmas carols or by the Negroes and so on and so forth. Once these new groups moved in they moved to the suburbs. Now this is a challenge and a challenge I don't think one can ignore. Bruno Bettelheim, in one of his most recent writings, refers to the challenge created by the need to be unprejudiced. We now have to accept neighbors we never expected to have to accept, and we will have to accept them in our schools and in our churches and in our neighborhoods and so on. Well, this is quite a challenge and if I think, for example, where on television I have seen people look worse than anywhere else, look more in distress, look more under strain, I can't think of anything aside from the racial situation where people appeared absolutely shook up and quite unhinged.

I have always been intrigued by the notion that we can work things out in figures; we can figure out the cost, the benefits of a change to an integrated situation versus the cost involved in the strain on those who are undergoing it. I think there is perhaps something to be gained in such approaches. I think in the end we will simply have to make difficult choices.

PANEL DISCUSSION

Dr. Auerback: When we started this panel I indicated that we would come up with some answers; that we were the experts; that we were the cleanup squad. What have we done for you? All we have done is try to put into focus that there are really lots and lots of problems. Whether it's the labor problem, the racial problem, the population explosion, poverty, or what have you, there are plenty of problems going on to act as reservoirs for more and more mental disorder and mental disease in years to come. However, we still have time and we are still trying, so at this point, we will take a stab at giving you some answers . . . maybe.

Question: Concerning more available work: should the basic pattern of the distribution of wealth be a proper concern for those concerned with mental health? Anticipating that a negative reply is prudent, if not necessarily logical, does this then imply that the focus which some see as a most necessary concern is close to creative endeavor?

Answer (Bittner): The question consists of two parts, the first part of which is answered in the second part. Frankly I don't know whether mental health specialists have any proper concern with the distribution of wealth. I must assume that the question implies that there is something wrong with the existing state of affairs and that mental health specialists might, could, or perhaps should do something about it. It should, of course, be remembered that large-scale social and political programs for redistributing wealth have been instituted in the Western World some decades ago. There has occurred a relative leveling of income, and the standard of living of all segments of society, but particularly of the lowest strata, has risen substantially.

Question: Please discuss briefly the comprehensive program needed to promote mental health in a group living in poverty.

Answer (Condliffe): I am going to transfer the particular location of this question, which I am sure is local, to an international setting with which I am a little more familiar. I have a feeling and have had it for many years that if you want to make contact in the poorest communities in the world in the underdeveloped countries, the key person is the village nurse. If you have a really competent, trained woman who can get inside the homes and talk to the women, particularly to the mothers of the little children, you have a beginning that you can't get in any other way. I have never understood why we cannot develop a real corps of competent nurses for visiting in our community as a professional group who would have access to the homes and be able to talk to those who control the homes. It seems to me that in these poverty-stricken communities, you can make the school not only the center in which the children can get a new view of life, but also make it a center from which the whole community can get a great deal. To tackle this problem of poverty, we ought to have the most beautiful and best staffed schools with the best specialists in the poorer districts, not where they are now—in the better districts which have many social facilities and resources. If this is done, then, in my judgment, it would be astonishing, how much self-help and how many cooperative projects would emerge in the community. To have one beautiful building would stimulate other efforts in the deprived community. It has a great deal of effect; I have seen it in different places overseas. Let me add one other thing; these problems are solved by the people themselves. There is nothing that we can do, great and rich and powerful as we are as a nation, to solve the problem of poverty in the world in all these overpopulated and underdeveloped countries, except by helping them find a way to help themselves. This is true on the international scene and equally true on the local scene.

QUESTION: Is it merely a myth that change or rate of change per se is a factor in emotional disorder?

ANSWER (GLAZER): I don't think it is a myth, but I am sure one can think of changes that do not have such an effect. But even changes that one might think do not produce strain, such as getting better jobs or improving oneself in the world, turn out to produce certain kinds of strains on people, adjustments, and new needs and so on. I think that in a rough and general way, yes, it is true, change in people's lives is a factor in emotional disorder. The point I was trying to make was that obviously some of these changes we want to happen, just as we want the defense budget to go down and we want the people of Appalachia to become economically productive and happier.

QUESTION: To deal with the problem of work morality, as an aspect of self conception in the face of the declining labor market, it has been suggested that the Federal Government provide a "minimum living wage" to every citizen regardless of whether he works or not and regardless of whether or not he is even interested in seeking employment. He will be deemed worthy of this because he is a human being, not because he produces or as compensation for not being able to produce. What do you or other panel members think of this?

ANSWER (BITTNER): What the question suggests is already, in a rudimentary sense, being implemented. The Social Security program and our eleemosynary system provides a minimum "income" for persons who are unable to earn it. Surely we could do much better in this area than we have so far. There also remains a good deal that could be done to redistribute work opportunities more equitably. That is, we could invent some methods whereby whatever little there is to be done will be done by all of us together. There probably are some ways in which one could make hiring labor attractive to employers, for example, by tying a firm's employment practices to its tax bill in such a way that having a large payroll would be more profitable than reducing labor cost. None of this will, in my view, rescue the value of work. The emancipation of our society from the need of such work as most people can do leaves lives empty and the gratis supply of income will not fill this void. To say that people deserve life chances without having to work is an empty gesture as long as in reality all the honor and dignity and distinction goes to those who work. After our needs are provided for we still need something to do that will earn us respect and offer us fulfillment.

QUESTION: I am questioned on my statement that our nation could afford to take care of all our people in their changing needs. How do you think our present economy will meet the challenge of our changing economy which you described?

ANSWER (CONDLIFFE): One remarkable fact about recent economic developments is that we have produced more food than we can eat with a constantly diminishing proportion of the labor force. California, which is a great supplier of food—the greatest in the nation—has only about one worker in 16 on the land. This process is going on in the heavy industry and will continue. It will go on in distribution, the physical distribution of goods. We have the resources and the manpower to meet our material necessities quite adequately and with a smaller proportion of the labor force. So we can spare the funds and the manpower, particularly the trained and the technical manpower, to work on and with the social problems of change. This is in fact what the Governor of California suggested the other day. Whether you can get the necessary attention to social issues from the organizations to be approached, we still have to see. We do have the technicians who could handle these problems.

QUESTION: How does or how should the public schools or community at large go about helping the culturally different Negro child overcome the effects of oppression and gain a more positive self image?

ANSWER (GLAZER): This is also one of those questions we could start a 15 day conference on and maybe I can say three or four things. Yesterday I saw the movie "The Cool World," which some of you may have seen, and there is a scene in which a white school teacher takes a class of ninth-grade Negro children on a tour of Manhattan to the Wall Street area, the Treasury building, and the statue of George Washington. Now the school teacher is clearly meant to be a caricature except that you know that when school teachers deal with 30 Negro boys, it's not a caricature; it's what really happens. This problem is that it's a disciplinary problem which is probably handled worse than it might be because if he had taken five boys on the trip, things might have been enormously better—he might have gained and they might have gained. I have to agree with Dr. Condliffe that we should put more resources not only in buildings but in personnel, into places where the school system is deprived. In Chicago there are magnificent schools in the Negro areas. The same is true in Holland where most of the rundown schools have been replaced by handsome and new structures. In addition to physical resources, we must consider human resources. Here we must learn from other countries. In the United States our poor areas are simply forced to go on their own; they pay teachers less; they have larger classes per teacher and so on. I was speaking to a Norwegian teacher, who told me that if he were willing to teach in the far north where it is hard to get teachers he would receive 20 per cent more salary. He was willing and that was why he was driving a new Volvo. Now this is a crude way of doing it, and I know that teachers in New York City refuse the notion of "battle pay," as it is called, for working in some schools. There are certain union reasons, which I did not understand. I think the issue is primarily more resources and then the complex technical question of how those resources are used. I would get more personnel, more buildings, more equipment, and supply preschool education. It means lengthening the school year by two months. This costs money, but we certainly can afford it.

QUESTION: How can the social structures and services that the mental health specialist and other interested people of the community are seeking to create or implement help society, especially if it has been directly or inferentially suggested that it is healthier to facilitate and coordinate rather than to control and insure conformity?

ANSWER (AUERBACK): Well, first of all I don't know how you make this a healthier or better world. I wish I did. Let me talk to you about a project in which I am involved. As you may have heard, I was introduced as Chairman of the Committee on Alcoholism of the United Community Fund. San Francisco has the highest percentage of alcoholism of any community in the country. We have lots of alcoholics and some 40 or 50 agencies, public and private, each in their own way doing something, in trying to tackle this problem. But each agency is going its own separate way. The United Community Fund felt that there was need for some kind of coordination, that a coordinated effort is possibly better than individual effort. The Committee was set up to try to coordinate the activities of these agencies. Any agency, whatever its nature, has usually been around for a long time and does not change very easily. Dr. Morris of Brandeis University says it takes from seven to 11 years for an agency to begin to change its mode of operation. After five years of involvement in this alcoholism program I agree with Dr. Morris that change comes slowly. Nonetheless, if you get people and agencies talking to each other, you develop lines of referral, areas of coordination, areas of community integration that previously did not exist. Our committee does not tell any agency, whether it is the Salvation Army, the Health Department, or the Council of Churches, how to treat the alcoholic because frankly we don't know. Nobody knows how to treat an alcoholic; each case is different. But nonetheless we are trying to get these agencies to learn to work together to break down their resistances, their hostilities, their competition.

Hopefully, we will create an attitude that might in the long run be more effective for the individual and the family with the alcoholic problem. There is no promise that we will accomplish a blessed thing with all this work. As a matter of fact, to my knowledge, no community has ever been overly successful in any program dealing with alcoholism, and time may prove that we in San Francisco have failed too. At least we will have tried. We are trying to prove that coordination works better than trying to impose rules. This is what we are doing in the mental health field—trying to get the agencies involved in the field to learn what other agencies are doing and how they can work together more productively. Hopefully each agency will find that area of the problem it is best equipped to handle and that other parts of the problem should go to somebody else.

QUESTION: Why has so little been said today about the use of recreational time and its use in the future? Will it not have great impact on good or bad mental health?

ANSWER (BITTNER): I don't know why the topic of recreation has not been discussed today. It would seem to be a glaring omission. Certainly the use of leisure time is very close to my own concerns, and the reason I did not bring this up was related mainly to the fact that I could not do justice to the topic within the limitations of time. In my view there is very little in what we today call recreation that is apt to fill the void created by the absence of work. At present the very notion of recreation is so closely tied to the notion of work that it lacks the substance to stand alone. There is little serious and important in it; it contains no discipline. I hasten to add, however, that this area deserves closer scrutiny than it has received and should be used as a source of inspiration for deciding what to do with idle hours.

QUESTION: Would an individual's participation in the decision-making process for their future welfare and adjustment possibly prevent going over the edge?

ANSWER (CONDLIFFE): Let me tell you about my experience as a teacher. I tried very hard for many years to get the students to do their own work. I gave them their final examination questions on the first day of the semester with a long list of references to read. The result of this was always that on the second day of class a student would say, "Professor, you set 1000 pages of assignments; how much of this do we have to read?" I then took the opportunity of saying, "If you know the answer to this question, you don't have to read anything. You read until you find an answer to this question." Then the second question came—it became a regular pattern, "How do we know when the answer we get will satisfy you?" My answer to this was very simply, "You'll forget my name five years after you are out of here; you won't remember anything about me, but you have to live with yourself for the rest of your life." At that stage I would lose about one-third of the class who could not face the responsibility of making their own decisions. The rest were worth working with. I cite this because I think we make a mistake believing that everybody wants to take the responsibility of sharing the decisions for his future life. There are many people who like to be told what to do and where to go; many have fear of the unknown. One of the difficulties about automation is that it has come rather suddenly. When something is introduced suddenly, and they can't see the ultimate result and how it is going to affect them, they develop more anxiety than when change comes gradually and they learn to adjust to it.

QUESTION: The spectrum of facets and disciplines covered in this seminar is most impressive, yet missing is one vital aspect of our changing communities—the powerful role of mass media in communication, information, and entertainment, as well as misinformation. Would it not have been appropriate to have had a speaker to discuss the role of mass media in shaping the minds and moods of their audiences?

ANSWER (GLAZER): I think it is a very reasonable subject. Probably in another conference this might well be taken up. Mass media certainly do have an influence on people, but it is very hard to measure the extent and nature.

QUESTION: May not the search for a definition of mental health be based on a false assumption that the properties called mental health have a universal quality? Mental health to have meaning must be considered as a part of a concept, a frame of reference, part of the cultural values of the society.

ANSWER (GLAZER): Many psychiatrists and anthropologists have argued along these lines. One anthropologist has written on this, indicating what mental health means in different cultures. At the same time others argue for the absolute notion that you can tell whether a man is mad, except in rare cases, in Japan, Africa, or Brazil. I will just leave it at that, since it is complicated and a debatable issue.

COMMUNITY FOCUS ON MENTAL HEALTH

Editors' Note:

Mental health is, of course, a concern of the medical community. Here Peter Cohen stresses the broad involvement of the medical profession, and especially the pediatrician, in problems of mental health. James Lowry gives new meaning to the term *mental hospital,* for he locates it on a continuum of community services available to aid the mentally ill.

Mental health is increasingly a concern of the larger community. In a variety of ways our social institutions—educational, economic, legal, and religious—are all integral to a community focus on mental health. Dorothy Westby-Gibson considers the climate for mental health in the schools and the role of the schools in educating for mental health and in serving students with special mental health problems. Lawrence N. Loban reminds us that industry, realizing that it lures "not just hands, but the whole man," needs research on the hiring of former mental patients and on what constitutes a good work climate. Richard A. Bancroft pleads for cooperation between psychiatrists and those who make, interpret, and enforce our laws. Clergymen, according to Robert Leslie, are increasingly better prepared to be supportive in their unique relationship to people in need.

THE MEDICAL COMMUNITY

By Peter Cohen, M.D.

The Pediatrician and His Role in Mental Health

During this century we have witnessed an amazing breakthrough in medicine and science. With the control of the diseases transmitted through water, milk, and food, there has been a marked decrease in death during infancy and early childhood. With the development of immunizing agents against certain infectious diseases and the availability of antibiotics for the treatment of bacterial diseases, further extraordinary changes are occurring in the morbidity and mortality picture in the United States. This has made it possible for the pediatrician to devote more time to the prevention of mental illness and psychosocial behavior. However, this is more difficult to accomplish than to prevent somatic illness. In the course of dealing with the child, the pediatrician is often family counselor as well as physician to the child.

To be effective in the prevention of mental illness the pediatrician should have contact with the family even before the child is born. It is an opportunity for the parents to meet the doctor who is to assist them in the care of their child. Information about the immediate neonatal period can be imparted to the parents, and pros and cons of breast feeding, for instance, can be discussed. After the child is born, "rooming in" service can provide for continuity and further opportunity for discussion of the management of the child during the first few days of life. There the mother can get to know her infant and his various idiosyncrasies, and any questions that she may have can be answered by the nurse and by the physician.

According to Erikson the early weeks of a baby's life are important in developing a "sense of trust." Although it is not possible to scientifically document the benefit of such concepts, the early establishment of a comfortable relationship is a step in the development of a sense of confidence and adequacy on the part of parents in raising children.

Not all infants or parents have a personal physician to whom they can turn for help with their many problems. Public health nurses and the community well-baby clinics can provide a similar service—in teaching parents the aspects of good care of their children. The public health nurse who is properly trained is sometimes in a more advantageous position to recognize influences which may adversely affect the mental well-being of a child, by virtue of her close contact with the family on many public health problems, including school problems of siblings. She has entree to the home, which provides an opportunity for insight which is not always available to the physician.

As the physician treats his patient he gradually becomes aware of influences that may affect the mental health of the child adversely as a result of family interaction. As the child grows from infancy through childhood and adolescence, he is sometimes exposed to traumatic and disruptive influences, on one hand, or to positive and constructive influences, on the other, either of which can influence personality. How he reacts will often depend on the parent and child relationship. It is quite apparent, however, that many children function well despite poor family backgrounds. This raises questions concerning the variation in individual vulnerability among siblings.

The importance of family dynamics on the mental health of the child, which the pediatrician has been aware of for some time has been receiving increasing emphasis by psychiatrists. Ackerman has stated that in order to build a program for prevention of mental disorder it would require, as a minimum, "family life education, social therapy, and psychotherapy of parents and the family group. Whether the preventive effort is grand and sweeping or modest, it must move forward toward a remolding of the dynamic functions of family life in order to supply the needs of children for healthy development."

The pediatrician and child welfare workers are concerned about the many children who must be separated from parents or parent substitutes. The magnitude of the problem is evident from the following statistics. "One out of every ten children is affected by family disruption resulting from divorce, desertion, or mental illness. As a result, there are approximately 7 million children in the United States living away from one or both parents; over 3 million require public assistance to stay with their remaining families; 175,000 are in foster homes; and 87,000 are in institutions. There are 2½ million working mothers with children under six years of age."

The mental health, child welfare workers, and pediatricians have been alerted to the potential significance of separation experiences as a primary cause of mental disorders by the comprehensive review of the subject by Bowlby. However, questions have been raised regarding the advisability of preventing separation at any cost. Bowlby himself has reported on the effects of institutionalization on young children which does not reveal the striking effects of separation which had been emphasized previously. It is not separation per se but, rather it is the degree of sensory deprivation that is important in understanding the varied and sometimes contradictory results reported as a consequence of separation.

Maternal deprivation to a significant degree can affect infants living in their own home. Richmond has reported on infants with problems of rumination related to mothers who maintained psychologic distance from their infants. Pediatricians and child welfare workers must continue to evaluate the degree of trauma experienced when a child is living with socially and emotionally disorganized parents against the alternatives which are available if he is removed from his natural parents.

THE PHYSICIAN AND THE MENTAL HEALTH NEEDS OF THE COMMUNITY

The concern of physicians in regard to the mental health needs of the community is revealed in "The Mental Health Needs and Resources in San Francisco," reported in 1958 by Watts and Babow. Responses to a questionnaire sent to physicians indicated that the greatest priorities in health care in San Francisco were:

1. Mental health problems, especially alcoholism.
2. Care and rehabilitation of the chronically ill and physically handicapped.
3. Problems of the aging.

It was interesting that 80 per cent of the physicians in this study made use of voluntary, public health and welfare agencies for assistance for their patients at one time or another. Seventy-five per cent of the doctors who expressed an opinion indicated that there was need in the community for more "residential treatment for emotionally disturbed children, psychiatric diagnosis or treatment, and institutional care of the mentally retarded."

This same report pointed out that there was an estimated 77,000 persons with some form of mental illness in San Francisco in 1957 (about one in ten)—15,000 to 20,000 were estimated to be under care, leaving between 50,000 to 55,000 individuals with some form of mental illness which was not being treated or was not getting any professional care. It is possible that some of these individuals were receiving aid from other services in the community—i.e., public health nurses, family and casework agencies or from workers in various public assistance programs.

POPULATIONS AT RISK

Physicians must be concerned with prevention of mental disorders and should be aware of certain groups as "populations at risk.' 'He may not be able to do anything specifically in regard to these problems, but he can be a leader in the community to help in providing appropriate programs for the following:

1. Juvenile delinquency—The best single criterion by which to predict which children are most likely to become adjudicated as juvenile delinquents

is if one or both parents were delinquents when young or are adult criminals. The second and best-known single predictive criterion was a broken home.

2. Attempted suicides—A study on suicide showed that 75 per cent of persons who completed suicide had previously attempted and/or threatened suicide.

3. Maternal deprivation—Children who are physically and emotionally deprived of mothering are definitely a "population at risk."

4. Families on relief—When welfare agencies are limited in personnel and budget, it has been suggested that emphasis be placed on the family which is likely to respond to short-term intensive work and go off relief in a short space of time, rather than spend too much time on those multi-problem families who can be expected to be dependent chronically.

5. Bereavement—Preventive work with surviving spouses and other members of the family of a recently deceased person may prevent a chronic grief reaction which may last for years and sometimes end in suicide.

6. Factors precipitating hospitalization—Prevention of unnecessary hospitalization for the elderly may be achieved by a team which works with the family and patient.

7. Promotion in industry—People who are about to be promoted to more responsible positions in industry are often a "population at risk."

CHANGING ATTITUDE OF PHYSICIANS TO THE MENTALLY ILL

We begin to see a change in the attitude of physicians toward the mentally ill, as well as the retarded. As improved methods of treatment develop, more and more of the mentally ill remain in the community or are returned to the community. Specific treatment has changed from the more traumatic procedures which included frontal lobotomy and electric shock therapy to the use of pharmacological preparations which appear to make many mentally ill patients more amenable to psychotherapy. This makes it possible for these patients to remain at home and within their community.

The community has to learn to accept them, to include them in their social life, their recreation programs, their industries and business. The use of "half-way" houses can be helpful in assisting the patient to re-establish himself in the community after discharge from a mental hospital.

Progress is also being made in improving local facilities to provide for the needs of the mentally ill in California and other states. The provisions of the Short-Doyle Act have gone a long way to assist and motivate local communities to do more for their mentally ill.

Paradoxically physicians have been partly responsible for some of the problems of aging by applying the technics of modern medicine to saving lives with the result that more people attaining the biblical age of 3 score and 10 and beyond. As people approach these venerable ages, many become infirm and some show deviant behavior. Are they to be sent off to an institution for the mentally ill because they cannot be tolerated by their families or by the community?

In some ethnic groups there is no question about the older individual remaining with the family. In our American culture, such responsibilities are often evaded and add to the deterioration of these individuals. Increased effort must be made to see to it that these people live out their lives as members of their own community and that they be provided with whatever physical comforts and emotional support they require.

CHANGING ATTITUDE TOWARD THE MENTALLY RETARDED

The approach toward the mentally retarded is changing also. Until recently, facilities for the retarded were limited to school programs for the mildly retarded and state hospitals for residential care for the moderately, severely, and profoundly affected. Beds have been limited and have not been available to all, which has resulted in long waiting lists. However, more imaginative programs are being introduced within the community. These include day care centers for those who cannot benefit by other established programs. Preschool programs, usually through the efforts of parent groups, are also springing up. More and more communities are providing special classes for the trainable, as well as the educable, retarded.

For some, when they have finished school, the State Department of Rehabilitation is increasing its efforts in providing an opportunity for vocational training. A limited number of the retarded are finding work opportunities in the community. For others, sheltered workshops offer varying degrees of services, according to the ability of the individual. Plans are being developed to provide residential facilities for those who require them, closer to their homes. The services outlined are still far too few and too limited in most communities, but the wave is developing and will continue to mount. When the physician is faced with the problem of counseling a retarded child and his family, he now has alternatives to recommend other than state hospital placement.

As the community changes, people who make up the community also change. Professional people, with their more enlightened approach to the problems they encounter in their clients, change each other. They also change the attitude of the people in the community, who then become more accepting of those with problems in the area of mental health. Finally, all of this hopefully effects a change on the recipients of all of this attention. This includes all of us—professionals and nonprofessionals alike, for none of us is immune to the problems we have been discussing.

THE MENTAL HOSPITAL

By James V. Lowry, M.D.

My subject, "The Mental Hospital," at one time would have been a rather cut-and-dried topic—simple, even, in some respects because of the stereotype approach. The term "mental hospital" meant *state* mental hospital. Today, "mental hospital" implies many things—24 hour care; day hospital; night hospital; with private, voluntary, or public auspices. Tomorrow's mental hospitals will be small in size and one element of comprehensive community mental health programs. They will decrease in both size and number as psychiatric services in general hospitals become more available, as more and more care is provided on an outpatient basis, and as more effective treatment methods evolve.

In order to describe future developments of hospitals, I will describe some current programs first.

California state mental hospitals have made important gains in the last several years in the race to stay ahead of the state's spectacular population increase. There has been a continuing reduction in the number of hospitalized mentally ill.

About 71,000 Californians receive assistance through department of mental hygiene programs every month. The department operates 14 large hospitals and two university-affiliated neuropsychiatric institutes. There are about 27,000 mentally ill and 13,000 mentally retarded patients. There are also three day-treatment centers and six aftercare clinics.

A second hospital resource is the state Short-Doyle Act of 1957 for support of community mental health services. This was California's first legislative recognition of the need for a breakthrough to bring psychiatric treatment services into the local communities. This is being achieved by making state financial aid available to locally operated public mental health programs.

Private psychiatric hospitals and licensed private institutions are a third type of hospital resource.

A fourth resource is the psychiatric service in private, nonprofit general hospitals.

There has been marked development and considerable achievement in all four of these hospital areas over the past few years. These expansions and improvements have much to do with the relatively good position we are in today to move forward toward comprehensive mental health services.

California is the most populous state in the nation, yet there are fewer

71

patients in the state hospitals on a per capita basis than any other large state. In 1963 there were 35,000 patients in California hospitals for the mentally ill—about 200 per 100,000 general population. New York, in the same year, had 89,000 inpatients, or about 500 per 100,000 general population.

The number of patients in California state hospitals is decreasing, though the state's population continues its unprecedented growth. In 1957 there were 14 million people in California and 37,500 patients in state hospitals for the mentally ill. The 1964 California population numbered more than 18 million, but the number of hospitalized mentally ill had dropped to 31,500—a hospitalization rate of 182 per 100,000. Despite an increase of 4 million people, there had been a decrease of 6,000 patients in California hospitals.

An interesting factor involves rising admission rates. With a greatly increased California population, there has been an increase in the total number of hospital admissions. An increase has also occurred in the rate of admissions per 100,000 general population. It has increased from 132 admissions per 100,000 in 1957, to149 per 100,000 in 1964.

Why this is so is a subject for speculation. It may be that people are more receptive now to seeking treatment for their illness, or it may be one or more of a half-dozen factors.

That our state hospitals have reduced their total number of patients is a real mark of accomplishment. It isn't because California's hospitals are unique among states in their richer staffing. California hospitals made this progress although they rank lower than 22 other states in the number of full-time personnel per 100 patients. They have managed to produce results *despite* the relatively low staffing.

Local community mental health programs have increased from seven programs in 1957 to 26 in 1964. During the last year these programs provided direct services to 58,000 people, and as many benefited through such indirect services as consultation and mental health education. The local mental health programs are located in areas in which 90 per cent of the state's population reside. Most recent, and particularly encouraging, has been the expansion of inpatient services in county hospitals under this program.

In 1963 only 10,000 of the 33,000 persons admitted to psychiatric wards of county hospitals received reimbursable treatment services. County hospitals were still functioning mostly as holding wards. In 1964, 37,500 were admitted and 22,600 patients received treatment services through Short-Doyle programs in their local hospitals. At present, almost five persons now are treated in local programs for every one treated in state programs.

In California the development of private psychiatric resources has increased similarly. This is of special importance considering the principle that the basic responsibility for meeting treatment needs rests with the individual, his family, and private resources. California now has more than 1,500 beds in private psychiatric hospitals. Other licensed private facilities such as nursing homes, day treatment hospitals, resident treatment centers for youngsters, etc., these now total 10,000 or 15 per cent of all beds in California for persons with mental disorders. That compares with the average of 2½ per cent for the nation as a whole.

The expansion in the psychiatric units in general hospitals has been as much revolutionary as evolutionary in the past five years. In 1959 there were seven such programs. They had a total bed capacity of 162, and they admitted 2,600 patients a year. In 1964 there were 26 programs, and their bed capacity was 725, and they admitted 11,600 persons.

I have discussed some current developments that will be important in determining the direction of change in mental hospitals in the foreseeable future:

1. The development of hospital services in local mental health programs with state financial assistance.
2. The growth of private psychiatric facilities, both special and as part of general hospitals.
3. Gains in health insurance coverage for mental disorders.
4. The increasing admissions to mental hospitals.
5. The decreasing size of state hospitals due to shorter lengths of stay.
6. The availability of alternates to 24 hour hospital care.

Two other factors will condition the changes—one is public understanding of mental disorders and an ability to accept patients with mental disorders as other sick people are accepted. The other factor will be the continued progress of medicine in developing more effective methods of therapy that will decrease the need for hospital care.

The state hospitals will continue to decrease in size. In addition they will develop small hospitals *within* the state hospital, to which persons from a designated geographic area will be admitted. An example of this is the 90-bed Napa-Solano Counties unit at the 5,000-bed Napa State Hospital. This is a joint program of the local community program and the hospital. It starts with the community services providing psychiatric evaluation for those being considered for hospital admission—with the hope that treatment needs can be met in the community. Fifty per cent of those examined were provided with alternate services.

All the Napa-Solano patients hospitalized come to their own ward—joining people from their own area, with whom they can identify. The ward treatment staff maintains close liaison with the community agencies throughout treatment. The agencies take part in treatment conferences—they participate in leave planning—and they assume a major responsibility in providing posthospital services on the patient's return home.

The state hospitals in California will become one element in mental health service area programs. Their functions will be in partnership with community services operated by local agencies. All mental health services (state and local) will be part of one service area program, rather than remaining independent services. In areas not able to support a local psychiatric hospital, inpatient services will be provided to several counties by a small state hospital as one element in the mental health service area. In this single-care system, complicated, organized line-crossing to obtain services can be avoided; a patient admitted to one element can be guided to all others as his treatment needs change, and there would be true continuity in his treatment.

As local mental health programs develop, preadmission examinations will be utilized to determine whether local resources can meet the patient's treatment needs. How can diagnostic screening reduce the number of hospital admissions? Only when the local resources *cannot* meet the needs will the patient be referred for temporary hospital care.

There will be continued progress in development of locally based posthospital services. This will allow expansion of leave programs for patients who no longer require hospital care, but who require assistance re-integrating into the community, programs now in effect through department and local auspices and which will be augmented to meet a larger share of the needs of this patient group.

These programs include foster home and boarding home care and work placement. A new project being undertaken by county welfare departments in California is the adult protective services. Through this program more of our aged mentally ill and adult retarded will be placed in boarding home facilities. This program is administered by the local county welfare departments with assistance from the Department of Mental Hygiene.

In California there are 13,000 patients in state hospitals for the retarded. About 4,000 of these could be cared for in residential facilities rather than in hospitals. If adequate facilities and funds for such residential care were available, our hospital population would be reduced to about 8,000 and our hospitals would be smaller in size and would meet the standards set by The American Association on Mental Deficiency.

There would be a shift away from the multipurpose hospital which provides hospital service, residential care training, and education that has been traditional for the four hospitals for the mentally retarded. Our goal now is based on analyses of the needs of hospitalized retarded and those on preadmission waiting lists. About 50 per cent of the latter could be more appropriately placed in other types of programs—were they available

These include nursing homes, residential facilities, foster homes, and other alternates to hospitalization.

Our plans include developing mental retardation service areas for the retarded. Each of the mental retardation service areas would utilize state and local facilities to provide for diagnosis and evaluation, family counseling, consultation to community agencies, outpatient medical services, inpatient hospitalization, day hospital programs, placement supervision in private institutions, foster home programs, rehabilitation and training, and research —the latter would be emphasized in programs with medical schools. There will be a single program for the retarded in the service areas, with the treatment needs of the patient determining the type of services provided.

The present four state hospitals for the mentally retarded will become medical care facilities in their mental retardation service areas. Plans call for other service areas, in conjunction with institutions of higher learning. The first two will be small units located in new programs at Langley Porter and U.C.L.A. Neuropsychiatric Institutes. They will be strongly research and training oriented. The program would utilize other community resources for the services previously mentioned. These would include all categories of residential care appropriate to the individual patient.

In the mental retardation service area program, we anticipate a decrease of 4,000 in present hospital beds and 2,000 new hospital beds in metropolitan areas by 1970. In the same period we expect an increase of 1,400 in family care placements. We also anticipate for this period:

1. An average increase in home leave of 100 patients a year for a net increase of 500.
2. In a new Department of Social Welfare cooperative program 1,250 placements.
3. Development of residential placements for 1,650 more patients now in Department of Mental Hygiene hospitals.
4. And placement programs for 1,700 mentally retarded whose requirements are for residential care, but who could be expected to apply for state hospital admission in the next five years.

The changes in the hospitals for the mentally ill and retarded in the foreseeable future will continue present trends:

1. Increased members of small local private hospitals and services in general hospitals.
2. Smaller state hospitals serving populations living within an hour's driving time of the hospital.
3. Greater utilization of alternates to 24 hour hospital care—day hospitals, clinics, foster homes, etc.
4. All mental hospitals, state and local, becoming one of the elements in a continuum of services to a specific population area.

THE SCHOOLS

By DOROTHY WESTBY-GIBSON, ED.D.

Recently a young kindergarten teacher asked for help with her new assignment—teaching remedial kindergarten. Not long ago at some 40 conferences sponsored by the U. S. Office of Education throughout the United States, educators expressed the opinion that children from nine to 12 years of age in our schools today show greater nervousness and have more fears, anxieties, and worries than children have ever had. Current reports highlight the increase in the number of adolescent suicides in the United States. Surprisingly—or not so surprisingly—college students with suicidal tendencies have been found as a group to be good or very good students. As one study[1] pointed out: "The bright students were often overreaching themselves, measuring themselves by their own standards, which were much higher and more demanding than the minimal standards of the University."

Evidence of the pressures on students today to get ahead academically is all around us. These pressures are moving downward through the schools so that even parents who have children in nursery school and kindergarten are worried about their academic progress. Students are obviously, as Dr. Peter Cohen has termed them, a "population at risk" from the mental health point of view.

In what directions, then, should mental health programs focus? Clearly, attention must be given to all facets of education. Let us here examine at some length the climate of the schools and then turn briefly to three other areas which deserve particular recognition: educating for mental health, the detection and referral of students with special mental health problems, and the provision of direct services.

THE CLIMATE OF THE SCHOOLS

Schools can provide a climate that helps or hinders mental health. The primary job of the schools is to provide an environment for learning, and the teacher's main role is to initiate learning activities. But "initiating structure" is not enough. To learn, children must see themselves as being able to learn. Teachers are key people in helping children develop feelings of self-worth and adequacy. All too often they build habits of failure and

[1] Clark, Marguerite: Suicide in childhood and adolescence. NEA J. 53:32-33, 54, 55, 1964.

feelings of inferiority that result in a lack of ability to learn. If teachers are to accomplish their goals for learning, they must be concerned not only with the environment for learning but also with the emotional climate of classroom and school. To use terminology borrowed from the analysis of leadership behavior,[2] they must be concerned not only with initiating *structure* but also with initiating *consideration*. "Initiating structure" describes those behaviors that set patterns of work and lead to achievement of goals; "initiating consideration" describes those that indicate concern about class members as individuals. Some teachers are high in initiating structure and low in initiating consideration; they are likely to be the autocrats of the classroom. Some teachers are low in initiating structure and high in initiating consideration; they are likely to be ineffective initiators of learning activities. To the extent that teachers can initiate both structure and consideration, can select learning activities and vary them according to individual needs, they are likely to be effective teachers.

All too often, however, teachers build habits of failure in students and contribute to their feelings of inferiority. Seymour Sarason[3] in his thorough-going study of anxiety in elementary-school children found that many children worry excessively about the many tests and quizzes they take in school—bright children as well as slow children. Unless checked, these fears and anxieties about school work can grow. He concluded that both parents and teachers play a major role in creating these fears and anxieties and that teachers are often unaware of the ways in which they are contributing to such anxieties.

Teachers, then, need to develop more self-awareness, more understanding of children and why they behave as they do, more understanding of what contributes to the learning process. Programs of teacher education, both preservice and in-service, must help teachers develop understanding of themselves and of their roles as initiators of both structure and consideration in the classroom situation.

More self-awareness can also help teachers understand how differently may be the expectations they hold for their students and those of the students themselves. Teachers naturally tend to view as problems those behaviors that deviate from their own standards. Most commonly these are middle-class standards which penalize children from lower-class backgrounds. Children from middle-class backgrounds, for example, as Jules Henry[4]

---

[2] Halpin, A. W.: The Leadership Behavior of School Superintendents. School-Community Development Study Monograph Series, No. 4. Columbus, Ohio, Ohio State University, 1956.

[3] Sarason, Seymour B., et al.: Anxiety in Elementary School Children. New York, John Wiley & Sons, Inc., 1960.

[4] Henry, Jules: Docility, or giving teacher what she wants. J. Soc. Issues 11:33-41, 1955.

has suggested, readily respond to signals transmitted by middle-class teachers; in his words, they learn to give the teacher what he wants. He cited, for instance, a fourth-grade art class in which the teacher selected one child's picture and held it up for the class to see. When she asked whether they saw the "nice" effect in the picture the children agreed. When she asked whether they "enjoyed" the lesson, many raised their hands in approval. Again, when she asked whether they would "do better next time," many also raised their hands to indicate that they would. As if on cue, they had responded to the words: "nice," "enjoyed," and "do better next time." The children obviously wanted to win the teacher's approval by giving the required responses. Sometimes, however, the children's inner signals would counteract the teacher's external ones, and the children would be unable to give the teacher what she wanted. Children, moreover, who are unconcerned with gaining the teacher's approval, or who are responding to different signals instead of being docile to the teacher, may be hostile. Teachers who are to work with children from culturally disadvantaged backgrounds especially must be helped to understand that these children may require different expectations on their part. In their concern for creating optimum climates for learning, then, educators are increasingly coming to understand that teacher-student relationships affect student achievement.

Some new research[5] in this area is proving especially provocative. It points to the relationship between the interactions of teachers and students and their effect on learning. Some students who are well motivated, in a word "strivers," appear to succeed with almost any type of teacher. But children who are hostile or vacillating or conforming show better progress (in science and mathematics, in communications skills, and in socialization) when placed with specific types of teachers. Such research leads to the possibility of a new basis for grouping students that might result in greater achievement for students and greater satisfaction for teachers.

No matter how effective the teacher is in interpersonal relationships, however, he too is highly vulnerable to pressures on all sides. In 1952, the Association for Supervision and Curriculum Development[6] commented:

> Teachers are pressured from all sides to teach this, not to teach that; to individualize instruction and help children socially and emotionally as well as intellectually and to do it in large classes of 35 or more; to use democratic

---

[5]Heil, Louis M., Marion Powell, and Irwin Feifer: Characteristics of Teacher Behavior Related to the Achievement of Children in Several Elementary Grades. Contract No. SAE 7285 Cooperative Research, Office of Education, U.S. Dept. of Health, Education, and Welfare. New York, Brooklyn College, 1960, mimeographed.

[6]Association for Supervision and Curriculum Development: Growing Up in an Anxious Age. 1952 Yearbook. Washington, D.C., The Association, 1952, p. 10. Reprinted by permission of the publisher.

methods and maintain a permissive atmosphere but not let children "get out of hand" or, for that matter, out of their seats; to give children materials which they can handle and let them progress according to their ability and maturation but cover the course of study and be sure that the class is up to grade level on the "national norm." Teachers are told to make the curriculum functional and to adjust instruction to meet the personal-social needs of children and then are given a standardized test to administer and are criticized if the children fail to demonstrate achievement in the traditional content material.

The situation today is little changed unless in the direction of even greater pressures.

Teachers, then, must be supported in their role by the attitudes and practices of school administrators, school board members, parents, and other members of the community. For the climate of the school is the product of all the relationships that affect it. In industry we have come to recognize the importance of high morale. In teaching, we have been less ready to recognize this.

Yet studies of school climates agree that, just as the teacher plays the key role in classroom morale, the principal plays a key role in staff morale. Teachers who see the principal as supportive of their efforts are likely to seek his help; those who view him as lacking in support try to avoid him. Teachers and administrators frequently perceive each other differently from the way in which each perceives himself. Principals, for example, report themselves as primarily interested in children's learning, but teachers view them as stressing obedience, cooperation, and maintenance of the good image of the school. Teachers and administrators, to paraphrase Flanders[7], can never avoid influencing; it is just a question of what kind of influence they will exercise.

Schools, then, contribute much to the learning opportunities and the mental health of their students by the climate they create. But schools also play other roles in mental health.

EDUCATING FOR MENTAL HEALTH

Some schools provide programs designed explicitly to educate for mental health. Some teach students about mental health resources in their communities. Children can be helped, for example, to understand why they feel as they do.[8] One third-grade teacher used a psychiatrist, who had a

---

[7]Flanders, Ned A.: Diagnosing and utilizing social structures in classroom learning. *In* The Dynamics of Instructional Groups. Nelson B. Henry, Ed. Fifty-ninth Yearbook of the National Society for the Study of Education, Part II. Chicago, Univ. Chicago Press, 1960.

[8]Wright, Betty A.: Helping children understand why they feel as they do. NEA J. 49:24, 1960.

child in her class, to lead a discussion on feelings. He focused the discussion on helping the children realize that their feelings toward their parents and their brothers and sisters were normal, that all of us, including adults, feel afraid, angry, guilty, sad, and happy.

Ralph H. Ojemann[9] has experimented widely with ways of helping children understand why they behave as they do. He has, for instance, developed stories that teachers can use in the elementary grades to illustrate differences between understanding behavior and passing arbitrary judgment on it. One such story is designed to help students appreciate the role of teacher as someone whose main responsibility is to guide learning activities rather than serve as disciplinarian. Ojemann has also been concerned with teaching social studies in such a way that children are helped to understand why people in different times and places have acted as they have.

Another approach to mental health education is reflected in teaching children about community resources available to help individuals and families with their problems. Especially at the secondary level, such teaching can help to dispel the stereotypes of community services as designed only for the indigent or of going for help as a sign of weakness.

DETECTION AND REFERRAL OF STUDENTS WITH SPECIAL PROBLEMS

No matter how concerned educators are with creating a climate conducive to mental health or with educating for mental health, some students will still have problems with which they need special help. Schools must, therefore, have effective programs for detection and referral of such students.

That teachers themselves can be largely instrumental in detecting these children was shown in a significant study by Eli Bower[10] of fourth-, fifth-, and sixth-grade children in California. Teachers in these grades, he found, were able through the use of various data, including mental ability and achievement tests, personality inventories, and a projective sociogram technique, to identify 87 per cent of the children diagnosed as emotionally disturbed by clinicians. Children with emotional disturbances constituted three per cent of the total number of children in these classes.

Teachers can also assist families and children in receiving special help. They can be aware of the resources afforded by school systems and communities and can encourage parents to take advantage of them.

What teachers do about mental health in the classroom, however, is only

---

[9]Ojemann, Ralph H.: Helping children understand why they act as they do. NEA J. 49:25-26, 1960.

[10]Bower, Eli M.: Early Identification of Emotionally Handicapped Children in School. Springfield, Ill., Charles C Thomas, 1960.

one aspect of the school's role in mental health. An issue that arises persistently is the extent to which schools should provide direct services.

THE PROVISION OF DIRECT SERVICES

Some boards of education provide no mental health services of any kind in their schools, usually on the premise that schools have no responsibility in this regard or that finances do not permit. Some support minimal services. Some attempt to offer as many services as budgets alllow.

A sharp discrepancy exists between the present availability and the estimated need for mental health services for children who are emotionally disturbed. Although it is estimated that at least ten per cent of school children need special help, mental health services are frequently lacking or inadequate. The most common service provided in the schools is that of counseling, but this is frequently undertaken only at the secondary level and then by counseling teachers who frequently lack specialized training and carry heavy caseloads.

The lack of other mental health workers shows an even greater disparity between need and available services. In a community which has some mental health services for children, it is estimated that a school system should have one psychiatrist for every 8,000 children, one psychologist for every 2,000, and one psychiatric social worker for every 3,000. To use the limited existing personnel most effectively, many school systems are making professional mental health workers available to teachers and administrators as consultants rather than using them to provide exceedingly limited amounts of direct services to families and children.

In a given community the extent of need for direct school services depends, of course, on the size of the community and the resources it provides. If schools are to implement prevention, detection, and referral programs, they must have adequate specialists to consult with teachers and adequate facilities to which to make referrals. If these agencies do not exist, schools and communities have to face the question of responsibility for the necessary expansion of community services.

Schools, then, have unique opportunities to provide integrating forces in the lives of their students. As the only agencies in our society which enroll almost all our children, the schools offer persistent opportunities for learning under the guidance of trained professional personnel. If these learning situations are effective, they can help students meet their basic needs and fulfill their developmental tasks. For the elementary-school child, successful school experiences can contribute to his sense of adequacy as a person. For the adolescent, they can heighten his sense of identity as an individual in a complex personal and social world. The child from a mentally healthy home situation can find reinforcement; the child from an emotionally disturbing home, new resources for help.

In this brief presentation of directions to follow in mental health and education, we have concentrated largely on the role of the elementary and secondary schools. But education does not stop at the classroom door or end at the graduation exercise. Education continues throughout life. Programs concerned with mental health and education must provide extensive opportunities for adults to gain the education they need. Some individuals in our society—teachers, physicians, nurses, social workers, clergymen, police officers, and others—are strategically located in the front lines of defense in mental health. Special preservice and in-service training programs must be pinpointed to their needs. On a broader scale, public education must be provided—education leading to new understanding and new attitudes that can contribute to sound mental health in the community.

Recently much emphasis has been placed on the quest for excellence in education. That quest must be paralleled by the quest for excellence in mental health in schools and communities.

BUSINESS AND INDUSTRY

By Lawrence N. Loban

It is axiomatic in modern industry that we hire not just hands, but the whole man. From the standpoint of the professional mental health worker, a job is a necessity for the maintenance of good mental health. From the individual standpoint, the requirements for full membership in our society include getting and holding a job—economic self-sufficiency. It seems to be in everyone's interest that we focus our attention on mental health in the industrial organization.

The employer historically has been outside the serious deliberations on the subject of mental health in industry. A history of mental illness, from a business standpoint, was automatically disqualifying when employment was considered. Now the employer is increasingly being drawn into such considerations, not entirely willingly. He has a number of reservations, in some of which he may be on quite solid ground. It should be useful, therefore, to consider some of these reservations and then point out some information gaps which need filling.

One reservation of the employer is that hiring former mental patients is time consuming. It doesn't take time to say "No," but it does take appreciably longer to assure oneself that the applicant is ready for employment now and will fit into the employer's way of doing things. Interviewers rarely have enough time to get the information they feel they need. Another reaction of the employer is that this is one more group asking him to give special consideration to one class of job applicants. He is already faced with requests from groups representing:

(1) The physically handicapped, with special groups for: tuberculosis, polio, the blind, the deaf, multiple sclerosis, heart conditions, and veterans —as a group. (2) displaced persons: Europeans, Hungarian refugees, and Cuban refugees, etc. (3) foreign student-trainees; (4) parolees; (5) minority races and religions; (6) over 40's; (7) retired military officers; (8) school students; and (9) mentally retarded *and now the mentally restored*. These, incidentally, are the worthy ones. There may be other and sometimes stronger pressures—nepotism and political considerations, for example. Viewed in this real-world framework, it appears the employer cannot satisfy everyone.

Still another objection toward hiring the former mental patient has centered on the possible effect on the employer's insurance program. It

83

seems clear that there has been no important effect on group hospital, medical and surgical insurance, or life insurance. The effect is less clear on Workmen's Compensation. There have been suggestions that former mental patients, who are hired and later become mentally ill again, may receive Workmen's Compensation on the grounds that the employment aggravated a pre-existing condition. The employer has a sound argument here. He says: (1) Those who have been hospitalized once for mental illness are more apt to return and (2) will stay for weeks or months, not days, and (3) will have a serious effect on Workmen's Compensation costs.

An additional objection is that the employer does not have enough statistical information with regard to how the former mental patient should be expected to perform.

Greatly abridged, these are some of the reasons the employer may give for resisting the hiring of the former patient. However, his exposure to mental health problems is far broader than hiring. If he has a payroll of any size, he has former patients on the job. He has some incipient ones, and he commonly has some who should currently be patients, whose illnesses are manifested by alcoholism, change of behavior, loss of performance, absenteeism, accident proneness, reactive depression, etc. These are his problem workers. Why should the employer resist help in dealing with these problems?

This is a new frame of reference. Now we're examining the way he runs his business. If we suggest, for example, that he should make a consultant available to his employees, we are in fact suggesting that he change his way of conducting his business. We are offering to alter his communications lines by providing another channel—besides the union—for bypassing management.

If we suggest the employer needs to alter the forces at work which interfere with interpersonal relationships, break down identification models, or raise the penalties for failure too high—if we suggest these things we are asking him to alter his decision-making capacity, his ability to act, in fact, his ability to get work done. The alterations involved can hardly be overstated. Most work is acccomplished through the process of accommodation, the subtle understanding that develops among people who know each other and accommodate by agreeing in some fashion on the division of duties. This is a system of power relationships and dependencies, formally set up by the chain of command and modified informally and made functional by trial and error and by custom. The system is not lightly changed.

If we present supervisors with techniques for using consultative methods for solving problems, they may agree and accept the methods in the classroom, but return to the job and continue using their old techniques, for a very good reason. If they switch methods of supervising it may confuse their workers, who are no longer able to predict their supervisors' reactions. It confuses their superior even more because he taught them one way of supervising, and now they are abandoning his techniques. So he calls his newly educated supervisors in and reorients them. The supervisors quickly learn that the way to please their superior is to forget what they got in the classroom. The only possible way to induce a lasting behavior change is to reach the superior first.

However we approach it, when a consultant proposes changes in the power structure of a business, or in the ways of satisfying the individual's needs for security or recognition or belonging, the consultant is posing threats to the integrity of the organization. In spite of these obstacles, it seems clear that changes would often be improvements.

Dr. Ralph Collins, psychiatric consultant for Eastman Kodak, has listed some of the reasons changes are needed:

"Emotional illnesses cause more absenteeism than any other illness except the common cold.

"Eighty to ninety per cent of dismissals today are attributed to social incompetence, the inability to get along with people. Ten to twenty per cent are defined as technical incompetence.

"One of four workers, or 16 of 65 million, manifest personality disturbances through absenteeism, accidents, alcoholism, illness, job dissatisfaction, or trouble with co-workers or supervisors.

"The cost to industry of the disruption resulting from emotional disturbances among workers, supervisors, and executives runs into hundreds of millions of dollars annually."

If he is to be a good leader, the health of the executive must be conserved, and yet today there are many pressures, frustrations, fears, and feelings of insecurity in his life.

Obviously, the employer needs professional help. There is a lack of communication between employers and mental health workers. The employer has too many unknowns, too many gaps in his understanding of the relation between mental health and the work environment.

This discussion has touched on two areas in which employers have reservations: (1) hiring and (2) on the job. These suggest some specific lines of research.

First, we may consider jobs for the former mental patient who is in the labor market. Some years ago, employers were understandably reluctant to hire the physically handicapped, on the apparently reasonable grounds that such people would be more sickly, have more absenteeism, be accident prone, etc. The Department of Labor did some extensive studies to reach toward the facts. These studies repeatedly showed that handicapped workers, properly placed, were not significantly different from the population as a whole. In some instances they were somewhat better than the non-handicapped. We have little in the way of comparable studies for the former mental patient. There have been many case studies, but these are more helpful to the professional worker than to the employer. What is needed are statistical reports.

Veterans Administration staff members have done an important piece of research that is relevant to this. They have published a study of some 1,400 World War II and Korea veterans with service-connected psychiatric and neuro-psychiatric disabilities. The employment data, gathered in 1960, show good job stability, with almost two-thirds having been with their employers five years or more.

With some reservations regarding the quality of this study, it certainly is a move in the right direction. We need many more such studies. We need nonveteran studies. We need to investigate a number of variables not accounted for here, which employers are fond of measuring. These would include, in addition to turnover, absenteeism and tardiness, productivity, accident frequency, and perhaps some measures of getting along with supervisors and fellow workers.

Answers to questions such as these, replicated in many studies, will dictate the approach of the professional workers to the employer. If the differences are not significant the approach will be on a straight businesslike basis; the employer should not arbitrarily restrict his labor market. On the other hand, if the figures show up unfavorably for the former mental patient, the approach will be to the employer's conscience—and he does have one. The appeal is that the way to be a good corporate citizen of the community is to take one's share, so that we may get whatever productive capacity there is in each individual and so that we may help people get "well" by providing work, which society considers necessary for full citizenship. Without underestimating the difficulties in obtaining data of this kind, the research can be done successfully.

Considering now the group mental health of the work force, we need another kind of answer. We need to answer the question, *what is a good work climate?* It is possible—if not probable—that some applied research would yield the information that certain large companies have a far higher incidence of employees entering mental hospitals than other companies. If so, why does it happen? Is it because employment interviewers and supervisors tend to hire to a corporate stereotype? Or do certain emotional syndromes tend to gravitate toward the employment offices of companies which project certain kinds of corporate images? Or is the corporate molding process responsible? Is the environment inside the company enough to make people ill? If it is the company environment, what are the causal factors and what can be done about them? Employers have not been provided with answers to these questions.

For that matter, are good mental health environment and productivity correlated? *If so, which way?* Does one cause the other . . . or are they related to other factors? We already know, through the work of Rensis Likert and others, that morale and productivity are not necessarily correlated. What pressures outside the work situation impinge on and affect overall corporate performance? Are the old mores relating to the values of work and the sinfulness of sloth becoming obsolete? Are they entering the realm of pluralistic ignorance? The problems of technological change have deep implications for mental health.

The employer will, in time, respond to professional answers to these questions. The number of people in industry with a positive desire to inflict injury on their fellow men is so small as to be negligible. The number who manage to inflict injury through ignorance is very large, indeed. Given the facts, employers will eventually adjust to them.

LAW AND GOVERNMENT

By RICHARD A. BANCROFT, LL.D., L.L.M.

A few years ago the Committee for the Continuing Education of the Bar, aided by psychiatrists and criminologists, conducted a well-conceived and well-executed course for lawyers on the "Human Behavior of Clients." Soon thereafter, and likely as a consequence, a basic and intensive series of lectures on psychoanalytic thought was offered to lawyers, psychiatric social workers, and others by The Psychoanalytic Institute of San Francisco. Lawyers of my acquaintance who participated in these courses were tremendously impressed by the insights they gained. They are, I believe, better lawyers for thus having been exposed to some aspects of, and the interrelationships between, certain of the behavioral sciences. For it is clear that lawyers and judges who write, interpret, make, challenge, and explain the laws—laws which are designed to regulate human conduct—should endeavor more fully to understand the human conduct which they would regulate. We in the legal profession can only learn from you who regularly engage yourself in research and education in the behavioral sciences and who appreciate the magnitude of the mental health problem.

It is no simple matter to endeavor to bridge the communication gap between lawyers and mental health specialists. I can be polite and say that the most readily apparent reason for the gap in communication is that the practitioners in each field are ignorant of the content, scope, and significance of the work the others do. Less politely, the harsh reality is that many lawyers and psychiatrists view each other and their respective fields with barely disguised contempt and function in an atmosphere of marked mutual disrespect, if not hostility and distrust.

I do not wish to analyze, or comment upon, the possible psychological reasons for the hostility shown by some members of the legal profession toward psychiatrists and psychiatry. It is to be noted, however, that since psychiatry is a young and still-growing branch of the medical profession, law and the members of the legal profession have, for a much longer period, been exposed to ridicule and contempt. Since long before the classic literary description of the law as ". . . a ass, a idiot," the legal profession has struggled to present a more appropriate image.

Basic to gaining respect for law and lawyers, however, is an appreciation of some of the limitations which proscribe the conduct of courtroom trial lawyers. Here, I deliberately omit reference to the law as applied by lawyers where they do most of their work—in their offices, counseling, advising, and negotiating. The sometimes comical image of the law is more often derived from that arena where the great drama occurs, the courtroom jury trial. Criminal jury trials, of course, gain the greatest publicity in this regard. It is from this arena—with its present-day extension by news and entertainment media, especially including television, that the legal profession is often demeaned and made to look ridiculous. The lawyers, of course, perform much more often and cooperatively with psychiatrists in the field of guardianship, wills, domestic relations, and so on. The acts of lawyers in these areas are much less often given attention.

The first and more important limitation is that our system of law is based upon an adversary system. Under it, in contested cases which reach the trial stage, lawyers are advocates who, in the courtroom, endeavor to present *only that evidence* which is favorable to their client's contentions. The assumption is that each lawyer performs this task of advocacy as vigorously as he can. What emerges from this contest, either by way of jury verdict or decision by the judge, is merely an *approximation* of truth or justice in a particular case, although it is said that law is "justice directed."

I know no lawyer or judge who believes that absolute or perfect truth in an individual case is established in these trials in an abstract sense. But rather it is contended by lawyers and judges that, on an average, the adversary system as we have it—involving as it does two lawyers pulling in opposite directions—more often succeeds in exposing the approximate truth than it fails to do so. The truth in certain individual cases thus may not be arrived at. But the likelihood of truth in the majority of cases is felt thus to be assured.

The adversary system thus makes trial lawyers look, to the uninitiated, like narrow partisans who jealously, and at times almost savagely, seize upon minutiae to exaggerate them out of all proportion. I am sure I have been guilty of this. Yet this is precisely the role the law casts upon American lawyers. And the ardent advocate staunchly and capably representing his client is indispensable to our liberties in so doing. To test this, just imagine yourself as a defendant in a criminal case where your ardent, stubborn, and obstinate advocate seizes on the minutiae to help you win.

Another area of misunderstanding has to do with the rules of evidence. Under these rules judges decide, after appropriate objections, what testimony, documents, or other evidence may be admitted into evidence in a legal proceeding. To the layman, and to many lawyers themselves, these rules seem frivolous and truth-frustrating. Indeed, in individual cases, it is quite clear that only the tip of the iceberg is allowed, under the rules, to emerge in the courtroom. Yet, behind most of the rules stands a great mass of persuasive justification for the admission and exclusion of certain evidence quite consistently with our maintaining the kind of democratic republic we enjoy in America today.

Of the same sort is the doctrine of precedents sometimes called by us *stare decisis*. This doctrine means that lawyers look back to the old cases. Thus, decisions are made based upon what judges have said long ago. This doctrine is most often misunderstood. Of course lawyers read the old cases—just as we read old books. And lawyers refer to the old cases as others, including lawyers, refer to old books. But in many cases *points of law* are very simple and clear, and there is no more specific reliance upon precedents than in any other discipline. There is reliance upon what is part of one's common understanding—based upon classic writings.

Usually it is *the facts* which are hotly disputed. In particular cases, where the interpretation of the law is doubtful, there is reliance on precedents by lawyers who must apply their skills by researching lines of authority and by reasoning from the decided cases.

There are many other legal concepts fundamental to our jurisprudential framework—too numerous to discuss or even mention—some or all of which contribute to the image some have of the law, or the trial, as a "spectacle," a "battle of wits," a "circus," a "game." The result of such an image is that some lawyers who participate in courtroom trials before juries are referred to as "buffoons" and "mountebanks." Yet it happens that precisely because of the presence of the jury very often lawyers are called upon to be consummate actors. But many lawyers—as a matter of fact most lawyers—do not perform often before juries. They function before judges without juries. They appear before administrative officials, and of course, they work in their offices. It is just a matter of overemphasis upon the role and activities of the trial lawyers in a few cases which provides the basis for the stereotype. Still the rules of law are a part of our reality, and although they restrict lawyers in the courtroom, especially before juries, and lay the basis for lawyer predictions to clients, they do not and may not so strictly confine the lawyer where he serves as a legislator, as a government executive or administrator, as an author, as a spokesman for cherished causes, or as a philosopher.

The preceding treatment is designed to influence you who deal with mental illness to react less strongly and with less scorn and less derision against the law's limitations and to invite you to appreciate and understand them so that your activities to influence the role of courts, lawyers, legislators, and government officials can be made more effective. Perhaps you can, by so much, influence more members of the legal profession to come to understand that diversity of opinion on psychiatric matters is desirable or that seeming lack of certainty in the behavioral sciences, called by some "vagueness" or "fuzzy thinking," is not a valid criticism.

The men who make, interpret, and enforce our laws clearly do not understand psychiatry and psychiatrists. We *must* before substantial progress can be made. Out of our greater mutual understanding and respect could arise the kind of cooperation I deem essential in dealing with America's mentally ill.

I don't know how broadly you define mental illness, but as a citizen concerned about the future of our state and nation, I am concerned about mental illness which manifests itself in acts dangerous to society requiring control. I suppose that is one of the reasons we have jails and penitentiaries—for the person who transgresses and must be held accountable by society. If he transgresses, he must account for his transgressions unless he is "insane" or "mad" under M'Naghten's Rules. We who are interested in mental health would add other words, and certainly we would add the word "sick." Under M'Naghten's Rules the inquiry is into whether one has a defect of reason from a disease of the mind preventing him from knowing the nature and quality of his act, and whether he knows right from wrong. Lawyers and judges, with the aid of the psychiatrists, have succeeded in only a few jurisdictions in broadening this rule or legal fiction to include the concepts of "irresistible impulse" and "temporary insanity."

M'Naghten's Rules are the law in California, although the cases of *People v. Gorshen,* 51 C 2d 716, set up a rule which the California Special Commission on Insanity and the Criminal Offender, in their first report dated July 7, 1962, recommended be placed in our code as follows:

> Evidence that the offender in a criminal proceeding has a mental disorder shall be admissible whenever it is relevant to prove that the defendant did or did not have a state of mind which is or may be an issue during the trial.

There have been cases in New Hampshire such as *State v. Jones,* 50 N.H. 369 (1871) and *State v. Pike,* 49 N.H. 399 (1869), setting up salutory rules; the Durham case rule or the "product rule in the District of Columbia, 214 F 2d 682 (1954), and the rule of the Third Circuit, the most and recent and most famous recent case, the United States against Currens, 291 F 2d 751 (1961). These cases begin to apply broader rules of criminal responsibility. The most inclusive rule is the Currens rule, as follows:

> The jury must be satisfied that at the time of committing the prohibited act, the defendant, as a result of mental disease or defect, lacked substantial capacity to conform his conduct to the requirements of the law which he is alleged to have violated.

This rule comes a long way from M'Naghten's Rules. Professor Diamond believes, however, that although this is a salutary doctrine, it won't gain broad acceptance, for neither the public nor judges will like it, nor will psychiatrists, whose mental hospitals would have increased loads.[1] It happens that I don't approve of its limitations to mental disease or defects. I am not sure that a sociopathic personality must result from a mental disease or defect.

As important as is criminal responsibility, and the legal rules under which forensic psychiatrists try to function regarding such responsibility, I am personally impatient to try to deal with mental illness in its broader aspects.

Beyond the criminal offenders who come to the attention of the authorities, there are those who never come to the attention of the authorities who are mentally ill offenders and who are never adjudged criminals, yet they are dangerous or potentially dangerous to themselves and to others. Beyond the paranoids and schizophrenics and those with delusional symptoms are the personality and character-disordered persons, the psychopaths, the sociopaths, and others in and out of hospitals and institutions. I am concerned about the alcoholics, the drug addicts, the unapprehended sex offenders, the juvenile delinquents, those unable to adjust and function in everyday life. The figures, if accurately assembled, would, I am sure, boggle the mind. Especially grim would these figures be if contrasted with the few available psychiatrists, psychologists, and members of other disciplines trained to treat the mentally ill.

I believe it is not simply a matter of lobbying for more money from legislators to build more and better hospitals, penal institutions, halfway houses, and other *structures*—although all these are needed, or may be needed, together with more doctors, nurses, technicians, and aides in allied fields. I believe it is not simply a piecemeal, part-time, charitable job which voluntary organizations alone can accomplish.

I believe it is the solemn obligation and duty of government to protect and cure the mentally ill. I believe that government and all individuals and groups vitally concerned should join together to educate the public to the vast losses in human resources, manpower, energy, and huge sums of money represented by the curable mentally ill who either are not being treated at all or who receive only adequate care despite the best efforts of the professionals in "people warehouses."

Although the Oakland City Council's alarm, reported in the papers recently, over the establishment by the California Department of Corrections of a halfway house in Oakland for San Quentin parolees can be understood, the resolution of the Council in opposition to such use of the house indicates how much progress is needed in educating even public officials. By the way, of course, I want to point out that particularly since the beginning of World War II, great progress has been made in under-

---

[1] *From M'Naghten to Currens and Beyond,* 50 Cal. L. Rev. 189 (1964).

standing the mentally ill, and even we lawyers have begun to learn a little about it. Still some official and professional reactions have hampered the rapidly growing Synanon movement to rehabilitate drug addicts. This program has been termed by many outstanding observers as an unusually significant breakthrough in the field of criminology and in making well those persons with character disorders manifested by drug addiction, the use of alcohol, and other symptoms.

It occurs to me that government, the professionals in medicine and law, and the volunteers who are concerned about mental illness in America should encourage and help such experiments, stimulate the bold and the new, and nurture and study all possibilities to improve methods of care and treatment.

If lawyers and judges knew how, they would help. You can teach them how. Urge the law schools to include psychiatrists and psychologists in their faculties. Approach the Bar Associations boldly with programs to educate lawyers for more effective presentation of psychiatric evidence and to aid in solving the problems in the field. Institute joint programs to develop better cooperation between law and medicine in the field of mental health. Maintain an atmosphere of intellectual diversity in your own field in which you challenge each other's conclusions. But don't fail to expose those in your ranks you consider intellectually dishonest who would carelessly, and perhaps callously, seek to discredit your entire profession.

I want to pose a question. How can the law be changed in this area of mental health? How can it be influenced as a practical matter? First of all, I believe that all things presently being done ought to be continued and expanded, but I think something more ought to be added. Laws change because lawyers try to make the laws change, and they try when they have a motivating force or a motivating organization behind them. It is no accident, for example, that on the national and state level it is possible for lawyers in the National Association for the Advancement of Colored People, despite the rule of precedents, to bring about changes in the law which have made the law more liberal and more reflective of reality. As a practical matter, it is not enough merely to approach a bar association and arrange a public seminar. In addition, if for example you want to change the M'Naghten Rule in California, the thing to do is to plan a comprehensive campaign. Approach the lawyers who are particularly interested and who are outstanding for their concern with mental illness. I don't mean the lawyers who are interested in solving the legal problems of mentally ill persons charged with crime. There may be 25 to 50 such, for example, in San Francisco. Have them called together, discuss with them what you think is a good rule for our courts to adopt. It would then be a simple matter for the lawyers to correlate their information as clients come into their office and to select a test case. Then a test case may be set up so that you would be more likely to get the kind of result that you want. Ladies and gentlemen, this is the way the law is made and changed in America and in every state in America.

After this is done, it is necessary to work out the tactics of the trial in great detail. It is important, for example, to time the case so that certain kinds of judges may be available to try it. It is preferable even to arrange it so that learned judges who have a background in psychiatry, persons like our own Superior Court Judge Gerald Levin, are likely to be in a position to make the ruling on the matters that are important. Thereafter, it is necessary to see that the evidence and the law are skillfully presented, together with the supporting psychiatric testimony required for the desired result at the trial level. Then it will be the responsibility of the district attorney to take the case up on appeal to establish that there has been some legal error. If the case is properly handled, the appeal is likely to fail.

I think within a short period of time it would be possible to have a better rule in California by far than the M'Naghten Rule, which was not even the rule in England at the time it was originally adopted. It was a restriction and narrowing of a rule which had much more beneficial effects.

In conclusion, the words I like to use in this area, as a lawyer—thinking to make it possible for our courts to adopt broader rules—are words like "incapacity" and "irresponsibility." If M'Naghten's Rules excuse persons who are "mad" from criminal responsibility, then I think we should contend that persons who are incapacitated to act responsibly should likewise be excused. I believe that to the extent that cooperative endeavor between lawyers and psychiatrists broaden and clarify these definitions, the problems of the mentally ill will come into sharper and clearer focus.

THE CHURCHES

By ROBERT C. LESLIE, PH.D.

The strategic role of the clergyman in preventive mental health has long been recognized. He ministers to people in the traditional rites of passage, particularly in times of bereavement and in other separation experiences. He intervenes, that is, he goes to his people on his own initiative rather than waiting to be called. He identifies potential difficulties in the normal course of pastoral administration while calling in homes and presiding over meetings. He understands his people through the perspective of a long-term relationship with them. He utilizes the resources of a concerned community in worship, fellowship groups, and action projects. In all these activities the clergyman is often closer to the needs of his people than any other professional worker in the community.

In spite of this unique relationship to people in need, the clergyman has seldom been perceived as a significant person by professional mental health workers. For many years the psychiatric world has acknowledged his presence but, on the whole, has ignored him when attempting to implement mental health plans. Characteristically, in the literature, professional workers in the psychological field note the supportive role of ministers but almost invariably go on to warn against the clergyman working with serious mental and emotional problems. In addition, the suspicion exists in some quarters that churches are for the emotionally immature and that religion itself is a manifestation of a neurotic pattern, but happily the mood is changing.

A very significant change in attitudes toward the religious world and toward the places of churches in community mental health has taken place in recent years. One manifestation of this change is found in the overtures being made by psychiatrists to clergymen, whereas in the past the traffic has been almost exclusively from religion to psychiatry; there are strong indications that a more nearly reciprocal relationship is developing. One-tenth of the psychiatrists in the United States, for example, are currently members of the Academy of Religion and Mental Health, an organization devoted toward bringing the psychiatric and religious world closer together. There are a number of reasons for this change in climate.

Ministers, in the first place, are better trained than they have ever been before for the pastoral care task. At the Pacific School of Religion we are helping ministers become alert to the opportunities for making use of psychological resources in their work. Most of our students are involved in programs of clinical pastoral training, some of them here in the Medical Center of the University of California, some at San Quentin, some at Vacaville, and some in other agencies. Across the country some 343 programs are assisting in such training, often in cooperation with theological schools. A new professional association, the American Association of Pastoral Counselors, is now developing standards for pastoral counseling as a specialty.

An even more significant factor is the growing recognition by the psychological world that the emotional problems of living as encountered today often stem from a confusion over values, a loss of a sense of meaning, a need for a clearer sense of direction. When, for example, Dr. Viktor Frankl lectures on logotherapy, he stresses the search for meaning as the most fundamental of man's needs today. The Protestant theologian Paul Tillich, who received very enthusiastic response from the larger psychological world as he spoke to many professional groups, talked about existential anxiety. By this he meant the kind of anxiety that remains after neurotic anxiety has been dealt with, as if to say that the very business of being human creates anxiety with which man has to learn to live.

Perhaps even more significant than these factors is the change in orientation many of us sense in the psychological world in which the focus of attention is on health. If the focus is on the ego strength, the potential capacity of the person to cope with life, this is the area in which religion has always been working. In his book, *Principles of Preventive Psychiatry,* which is strongly oriented to community psychiatry, Dr. Gerald Caplan makes the point that although reactions to handling crises have commonly in the past been related to personality structure itself, a new trend is to stress the kind of support made available in the community. Obviously the clergymen and the church organization which he represents can provide a major portion of that kind of support.

The clergyman has access to people in crisis in a way that is seldom open to other professional workers. You recall the finding of the Joint Commission on Mental Illness and Health, a rather unexpected finding that of the Americans who seek help with their emotional needs, 42 per cent turn first to their clergyman. Whereas the Joint Commission interpreted the greater readiness to turn to clergymen rather than to psychiatrists as indicating a reluctance to accept responsibility for really working on emotional problems, it may also be true that people in general see themselves as basically healthy and are looking for help in using their own strength rather than in delving into their weaknesses. Most parishioners are able to talk to their clergymen about their own needs without feeling that they are putting themselves in "treatment." They can consult with their minister and feel that they are handling their own lives. A part of my job is to help make sure that ministers are better trained and better qualified to aid their parishioners when they turn to them. Moreover, people are likely to find in their clergymen a personal warmth and a personal responsiveness which may in the long run be more important than better trained professional help. It seems clear that one of the growing edges of the psychological world today is to ask some searching questions about how effective an impersonal professional stance really is in working with people.

Certainly it is to the discredit of the churches that so little has been done in the mental health field, but there are hopeful signs. Across the country pastoral counseling services are being organized. Currently there are 173 of them with about two more starting every month. This means about 18 a year coming into existence, a situation causing genuine concern for those who are professional in the field, but at the same time presenting a new opportunity for direct service to people in need. Many centers spring up in metropolitan areas where the need is not so great, where they serve largely in a referral capacity, but others are opening in communities with no other resources currently available.

A second trend to be noted in churches throughout the country is the development of small groups, groups characterized by intimate interaction with a considerable amount of sharing on a personal level. These are not therapy groups; they are study groups, action groups, or prayer groups, but many of them carry highly significant therapeutic overtones. In our dehumanized and alienated culture, the opportunity for coming together in intimate group life serves a very genuine purpose.

Still another trend, and one in its very beginning stages, is seen in the efforts of churches to go out from their buildings into the community. A number of churches are experimenting, for example, with an outreach program that centers in a coffeehouse where people come together and are able to establish a feeling of community in a place outside of the traditional church building. Here the pursuit of ideas and the struggle for help is carried on in a significant although unorthodox way. A number of projects are being developed in churches alert to their mental health responsibility: halfway houses for former mental patients and retreat centers for people with special needs. One church was instrumental in establishing a family service agency in a community that had none; another, in developing a community psychiatric center here in San Francisco. Plans are now under way for developing a night call service where people with special needs can call in to talk with someone about their problems.

The churches are working slowly and often not effectively, but they are working. Where the leadership needs in the community are so great and where it is so important to find channels through which access can be found to make contact with people in need, the churches can provide one of the unused resources available to all of us.

DEVELOPMENTAL APPROACHES TO MENTAL HEALTH (THE SEARCH FOR A SOLUTION)

Editors' Note:

In the search for solutions to mental health problems many approaches are possible. In this section the approaches are developmentally oriented. Theresa Mahler begins by viewing the pressures on children and youth today and then develops a series of new perspectives on the provision of financial resources and of programs and services for children and youth. Perhaps, as she concludes, "The increasing coordination of effort" may lead "to a willingness to spend more money for prevention and therefore less for cures."

Paul Watzlawick places the crucial uncertainties of the young adult years in the context of the family and the society in which they occur. He sees the potential for their solution in the development of the ability to accept and tolerate change.

The middle years, on the one hand, brings a time of responsibility and potential stability and, on the other, a "reluctantly accepted position of impending decay." Klaus Berblinger urges that those facing emotional stress in these years must be helped "to find *actual* solutions to *obsolete* problems" rather than "to deal with *actual* solutions in an *obsolete* way."

Marjorie Fiske Lowenthal finds our conflict about aging confounded by our conflicts about leisure. She reports what has been learned through recent research on the interaction, isolation, disengagement, and escape of the elderly and points to some directions for successful aging.

A NEW PERSPECTIVE FOR CHILDREN AND YOUTH

By THERESA S. MAHLER

1. THE SEARCH FOR SOLUTIONS

The potentials for solution to any given problem vary, depending on the focus, or bias, of those who propose solutions. We must continue to search for solutions, but all too often we look for panaceas, for the magic pill to cure the pain.

Sometimes in the search for solutions we are inventive and creative, as in the proposal made by Governor Brown* to "harness the efforts of the State's most talented aerospace engineers . . . to apply their sophisticated, computerized, analytical techniques to solving the State's major problems, including:

1. State-wide transportation.
2. Analysis of the social structures of prisons and mental hospitals.
3. Collecting, storing, and utilizing masses of information on the State's functions, including health and education.
4. Disposition of wastes in land, air, and water.

Governor Brown proposes to utilize their talents "to think in terms of new dimensions, break down barriers and proceed along new technological lines."

Original thinking is also evident in the proposal made by James Bryant Conant, president emeritus of Harvard, in his new book, "Shaping Educational Policy," in which he says, as one writer reports it, "Don't leave education to the educators." Dr. Conant wants a commission composed of distinguished citizens who are not educators to plan national educational policy. He warns us, also, not to leave education to the legislators.

We find the idea of an earlier start in education, proposed by many, carried perhaps to an extreme in the words of Commissioner of Education Francis Keppel, who is quoted as saying in a recent speech before the Council for Basic Education: "Throughout the country, we are beginning to harvest the results of experiments in creative schools *where 2 and 3 year old youngsters are learning to read and write,* where first graders are learning the fundamentals of algebra, where second and third graders are becoming

---

*Edmund G. Brown, Governor of California.

familiar with relativity physics, where fourth and fifth graders are learning to employ 'set theory' in mathematics."

Or, do we wish to adopt the kind of solution proposed by the British National Union of Students to a government commission that children should begin school at 2?

Depending on our own particular focus or bias, we might accept any one or all of these proposals as "potentials for solution" to some of the problems we face today in the family, the school, the community, the society—there is no doubt that in each proposal there can be found areas of merit and disadvantage.

We are reluctant to offer solutions, yet we feel the pressure of the problems, and the even greater pressure of needing to "do something." We've all heard or used the expression, "Let's take a new look at the problem." What are the new perspectives in relation to some problems we face?

2. WHAT ARE SOME NEW PERSPECTIVES IN RELATION TO THE PROBLEMS WE FACE?

Let us consider some of the anxieties and pressures which impinge upon our mental health today. A survey made by the Bureau of Elementary Education of the State Department of Education showed some interesting results. Elementary- and secondary-school principals, faculty members in teacher-education institutions, officers of parent-teacher associations were asked to express their views on the major areas of pressures for children and youth today. They summarized the pressures as follows:

(1) Fear of the future; (2) demands to get ahead academically; (3) unrealistic demands for scholastic achievement; (4) demands to push advanced curriculum in lower grades; (5) demands to lay on the homework; (6) competitive race for college; (7) demands to get ahead socially; (8) overcrowding the lives of children; (9) conflict in values; and (10) questionable school practices.

In an address given before the National Conference for Support of Public Schools, John Kenneth Galbraith, Professor of Economics at Harvard University, in speaking on "Education and Poverty," said that recognition of the need for education for a large majority of our people has brought about *anxiety about college admissions.* Back of this is the concern about the quality of education on the primary and secondary levels—and now we are feeling the pressures even in the nursery school and kindergarten.

"Tension will increase," said Dr. Galbraith. "Those who stand for economy, ignorance and the McGuffey readers will be swept aside. . . . the volume of our resources going into education must be increased."

How to get our riches into action in education is indeed a problem. Should this be through federal aid to education? The concept of federal aid to education is not a new one. The first legislation granting aid to education, enacted in 1785 as part of the Ordinance of 1785, set aside grants of land for support of the common schools. In the 179 years since then, Congress has passed almost as many bills as there are years providing aid to education in one form or another.

But there are still major blocks to the passage of desirable federal legislation, and these are not on the basis of need or fear of federal control. The three major issues are: (1) The question of granting public funds to church-related schools; (2) desegregation; and (3) the criticisms of expanded federal spending.

Now there are many kinds of federally funded specific aids: the Manpower Development and Training Act, the Economic Opportunity Act—to mention only two recent programs—but in providing for these special categories there is often duplication of services. Even more frequently tremendous gaps between services occur, into which those who need the educational assistance may fall and be lost.

One solution that has been proposed by the top economic strategists of the Administration, led by Walter Heller, former chief economic adviser to the President, is that state governments should receive 1 per cent of the taxable personal income after deductions and exemptions, as a straight grant, with no strings attached. This would amount in 1965 to 2.5 billion dollars to the states from the federal government. Two-thirds of each year's lump sum would be assigned on a straight per capita basis to each state, and the other third would be distributed as an extra to about a dozen "poor" states, presumably in the South.

Providing the funds, whether locally, on the State level, or from the Federal government, for school buildings, for the education of more teachers, for special programs, is not a "solution" to all of the ills of education, to the problems of providing more and better schooling for our children, or to the problems of mental ill health.

We can, with our tremendous resources, make good education available to all, but we must go back and take a look at the individual and ask whether he is ready to benefit from what is offered.

How do we go about orienting our children—especially our youth—to want the education available to them? How do we orient them to plan for the future? Parents and teachers are eager to help—often oversolicitous in trying to help children avoid the mistakes of their elders. Adults frequently urge youth to set impractical goals, which are not objective in terms of their capacities and interests or of the structure and needs of society.

It is easier to give advice in generalities than to pinpoint advice in specific circumstances. With the now-existing pressures regarding college entrance, our children must decide much earlier on what "track" they are going to travel. This means not only more and better counseling in the schools but a more realistic attitude on the part of parents. Should every boy and girl in junior high today be headed in the direction of college—and if so, is science the only field for him? Do we expect too much of our children or not enough?

Intensification of counseling and guidance services should be one of our goals. Use of social workers in some high schools has extended the services of the guidance counselors. More realistic counseling regarding courses of study is essential, though this is easier said than done in view of the many rapidly occurring changes in curricula.

For early identification and treatment of children with special problems, we cannot rely only on psychologists and psychiatrists. Parents, teachers, physicians, pediatricians must become more aware of the significance of behavior which may, even in the child's earliest years, be indicative of more serious problems later on. We need to be sensitized to the evidence of behavior which reveals emotional disturbance. San Francisco, with all of its fine resources, is probably meeting the needs of only about 25 per cent of the emotionally disturbed children and their parents who require psychological or psychiatric services.

If we need to be more realistic in counseling, so that our girls and boys will set achievable goals, can we still find ways of helping them retain and strengthen their youthful idealism? We need to improve our methods of teaching mathematics and science, but we must also do more in the area of teaching about "people problems." We cannot do this kind of teaching in a vacuum, and it is not the kind of teaching which is done only in the classroom. Families, schools, and the community must share the responsibility. We must become involved and we must involve our children, particularly the young adolescents. The junior-high and early high-school years are the period when youngsters want to help. They want to be dedicated. They want to feel big and important and needed.

Involvement of teen-agers in community services is not a new idea. But the use of the younger adolescent—the junior-high girl or boy, the beginning high school student—this is a fairly unexplored field. Beginnings have been made by some lay groups and community organizations. For instance, the American Red Cross in its Youth Department finds ways of channeling the interest, energy, and enthusiasm of the young teen-ager into service in such areas as water-safety aides, service to the ill or aging in convalescent homes, tutoring of elementary-school students. These are only a few of the possibilities. Much more can and will be done when institutions and agencies express a willingness to lower the age barrier for these youngsters who are so willing to perform worthwhile work.

Automation and social change make preparation for achievement increasingly specialized and expensive and also make appraisal of what the individual's future should be much more difficult. The times demand more flexible goals for our boys and girls, if they are to be helped to maintain good mental health. If we must concede the fact that automation is demanding more highly specialized learning, that not all of our children will make the grade for entrance to university and college, then we must be flexible, too, in finding new areas in which they can gain recognition and experience a sense of achievement.

Automation, the population explosion, the demand for more and better education for each and every child have combined to exert pressure all the way along the line in education. The elementary schools no less than those on the secondary level are being scrutinized and analyzed and criticized. Within the schools there is a surge of experimentation and exploration to find new and better—and more flexible—ways of meeting the needs of the children in the "middle years." Films, film strips, tape recorders, along with textbooks and the phonograph, have long since been accepted as routine aids to instruction. Educational television is in use in many school rooms across the land. School housing planners must add to the cost of new buildings the installation of outlets in every room and antennas on the roof. Teaching machines are feared by some and praised by others. It is perhaps too early to say whether mechanized teaching is one of the potentials for solution to the problem of masses of children before us to be taught.

Another means of achieving greater flexibility in our teaching methods may be the utilization or adaptation of the principles of the nongraded system in elementary schools. This is not a new perspective, for the idea has been around a long time, but the use of this system is coming into focus again. In the opinion of proponents of the nongraded school, the question is not "what is the child supposed to do?" but "what learning opportunities are most appropriate if the child is to achieve his maximum potential?" This is certainly what an excellent teacher asks and tries to provide in any classroom. But whether in a nongraded or graded school, this attention to the needs of the individual is predicated upon smaller class size, and that means additional costs. At present, the nongraded school is most likely to be tried at the primary level. In a few communities the plan is being tried in the upper elementary grades, and there is some consideration being given to the possibility of extending the idea, at least to some extent, into junior- and senior-high schools.

Another new perspective is the recognition of differences in the kinds of intelligences. Research carried on within the past five years with children from nursery-school age to adolescence has led to a changing concept of mental function. Some researchers believe we can find ways of determining much more specifically just how the individual thinks and what kind of knowledge he can handle. Most intelligence tests emphasize perception and recognition of a problem (cognition), memory, and use of the information perceived and retained (convergent thinking). But they give little opportunity for the demonstration of inventive and evaluative thinking. Parents, teachers, and pupils tend to believe the creative thinker is an "odd-ball," and certainly he can at times be difficult, whether in the home or in the classroom. The child who is able to do creative thinking is not always the one who scores high on the standard intelligence tests. Yet he must be identified, if we are to utilize his potential to the fullest extent.

We are beginning to realize that memorizing information for the sake of information alone is not enough, for the computer can accomplish this better and faster than the human mind. We do not yet know how much of each of these intellectual factors which comprise the total human mental process is determined by heredity and how much by learning. But it would be safe to say that to some extent every intellectual factor depends on learning. We should, therefore, provide practice at every educational level, beginning with the very youngest child in the home, for all types of intellect, including the much neglected kind of thinking that takes off in new and different directions, that senses deficiency and aims at improvement.

This creativity is often discernible very early in the child's life. In fact, many a parent of a two- or three-year-old wishes that he were not quite so creative in his activities. Today's reanalysis of our entire educational system reveals the early years of childhood in a new perspective. A widespread concern over this question of providing quality education for all of our children has filtered down into the kindergarten and the nursery school. Extensive research in connection with finding ways to help the culturally disadvantaged child has re-emphasized what has been known for many years—that the child does not wait to begin learning until he sets foot in the door of the kindergarten or the first grade. Throughout the country there is an upsurge of interest in prekindergarten education, whether it be offered in a good nursery school, a day-care center, or in some other type of organized group activity for children below kindergarten age. In fact, there is concern among some professional people who have worked in the field of nursery and early childhood education for 20 or 30 years about the fact that anybody and everybody now wants to save the day for the culturally disadvantaged, the school dropout, and the harrassed classroom teacher, by getting Johnny and Mary into a good nursery school, and there, between the ages of 2½ and 3 and 5 or so, the magic transformation will take place. The recognition of the importance of the early childhood years, the eagerness of parents, professionals, and lay groups to "get something going" to establish prekindergarten groups must be accompanied by thought-provoking attention given to establishment of standards, preparation and certification of teachers, and provision of adequate funds so that the job can be well done. We need to remember that if the early years are of imperative importance as the foundation for later success in the child's more formal schooling—and they are—then these years must be safeguarded against unwise exploitation, such as trying to teach the three-year-olds to read and all four-year-olds to master the new methods in mathematics.

More and more research is pointing up the fact that for the majority of human beings, the patterns of learning are probably well established before the child enters school. This is not to say that every child must now be enrolled in a nursery school or in school, as the British Students Union recommended. Children have in the past laid this basic foundation for learning in the home and at the mother's knee, so to speak. But the family today—with the complexity of pressures upon it, with its possible limitations of space, resources, and parental time—no longer meets all the needs of every prekindergarten child. As a matter of fact, although kindergartens have been established in this country for about 100 years, only 40 per cent of our five-year-olds have public school kindergartens available to them. Nursery schools are almost half a century old in America, yet at the present time they are available to very limited groups of children. For instance, parent cooperative nursery schools are limited to those children whose mothers are free to participate as a part of the parent-education program carried on in conjunction with them. The California Children's Centers are available only to the children whose mothers are employed. And there is a growing army of these mothers and an increase in the number of children who require this service. There is talk now of including some "pilot programs" for preschool children in the planned expansion of the McAteer Compensatory Education Act. (Why "pilot" when we have 50 years of proof that nursery-school experience is beneficial to children, and especially when they come from families who for socioeconomic reasons are not able to provide the rich experiences that children need at this period of their growth?) But we are a long way from that possible solution of providing more and better education for every child earlier in the life of that child through nursery and kindergarten education, because this solution, too, will cost money.

Perhaps the best potential of all is the increasing coordination of effort among professional and lay groups, between parents and teachers, among the many interested individuals in any given community who are concerned with children. Together they may bring about changes in attitudes, leading to a willingness to spend more money for prevention and therefore less for cures.

UNCERTAINTIES FOR THE YOUNG ADULT

By Paul Watzlawick, Ph.D.

The problem besetting the young adult in his attempts at finding his place in life, his uncertainties and his quest for solutions, have been the object of many detailed studies from a good many points of view. Developmental psychology, psychoanalysis, sociology, existentialism have all contributed significantly to our objective knowledge of young adulthood, and to this we each can add our subjective experiences during this period of our lives. Still, it seems that the uncertainties persist and that solutions are more desperately needed than ever before. Needless to say, this paper cannot be more than an attempt at presenting the same problems from a somewhat different viewpoint, and in order to do this I shall draw on some of the results of the work carried out in recent years at the Mental Research Institute in Palo Alto.

It may be a platitude to state that young adulthood is a period of significant *change*, for, strictly speaking, all life is change. But the changes inherent in young adulthood are of a complexity which is probably second only to the changes and adaptations necessary during the first 18 months in the life of the human organism. Even more, change—a term constantly used in developmental psychology and psychotherapy—is a very difficult concept. Does it refer to something which at all times was potentially present? In my opinion one cannot deal with any specific period or area of change unless one has asked the more general question: what is change? That is, it depends on the answer to this general question what kinds of answers will be found in any particular period of change, such as young adulthood. For undoubtedly an observer's outlook will be governed by his general perspective, and this will in turn determine whether he will see continuity or discontinuity in the process of change. Curiously, however, the same viewpoints are not consistently applied to the study of change in the human being. The changes in, and the adaptations of, the very young organism are quite naturally seen in terms of a constant interaction between this organism and the environment. But the analogous processes in later life are traditionally and predominantly seen much more as something occurring in the solitude of his mind—as *intrapsychic* processes. This is not the place to speculate why different conceptual frameworks should be applied to essentially analogous phenomena. Suffice it to say that this conceptual divergency becomes particularly noticeable in connection with so-called disturbed behavior. If such behavior is viewed in isolation, the only conclusion that can be drawn from it is that the mental faculties of the individual have somehow suffered and that his behavior is the result of this impairment. But what is "disturbed" and what is "appropriate" behavior is ultimately determined by the context in which it occurs. To exemplify: In his delightful book *King Solomon's Ring*[1] Konrad Lorenz describes his imprinting experiments with young ducklings. He had substituted himself for their mother and then found it necessary to continue to crouch in front of them for several days:

"I was congratulating myself," he writes, "on the obedience and exactitude with which my ducklings came waddling after me, when I suddenly looked up and saw the garden fence framed by a row of dead-white faces: a group of tourists was standing at the fence and staring horrified in my direction." For the ducklings were hidden in the tall grass, and all the tourists saw was the totally unexplainable, indeed insane behavior of a middle-aged man, dragging himself, crouching, round the meadow, glancing constantly over his shoulder and quacking without interruption.

This difference between focusing on individual behavior in artificial or accidental isolation, or on that behavior in its wider context, is analogous to the conceptual divergency mentioned.

Essentially the same situation arises during Asch's famous experiments[2] when one unsuspecting and uninitiated subject has to affirm his perceptions in a very simple test of visual discrimination in the face of massive group disqualification by several other pseudosubjects briefed to give unanimously the same wrong response. Asch found that approximately 75 per cent of all subjects sacrificed confidence in their own perceptions in favor of the (wrong) response given by the other "subjects," and many of them did so under great internal stress which sometimes bordered on a feeling of depersonalization. Again, if the behavior of these subjects were viewed in isolation, a psychiatric label could be applied to it, and the reason for it would have to be sought in some intrapsychic disturbance. If, on the other hand, the whole situational context is taken into account, the phenomenon clearly reveals itself as a particular *organism-environment interaction*.

What has all this to do with the uncertainties of the young adult? The answer is that these uncertainties and the typical problems of young adulthood are very often of the same nature excepting, of course, such disturbances which are clearly of organic origin.

It should not be construed from the foregoing that change and pathology are being treated here as related concepts. Not only is this symposium

[1]Lorenz, Konrad Z.: King Solomon's Ring. New York, Crowell, 1952.
[2]Asch, S. E.: Studies of independence and submission to group pressures. Psychol. Monogr. 70, No. 416, 1956.

concerned with mental *health*, but the phenomena of change and the uncertainties prompting or accompanying change can, of course, be observed in the healthy much more frequently than in the sick—not only because fortunately there are more well than sick people, but also because flexibility and adaptability are outstanding characteristics of a healthy organism.

A child's conception of the world is basically one according to which his own small world and the world at large are identical. Or, to put it slightly differently, he assumes that what happens in his family happens all over the world. Together with this goes a subtle, but highly complex indoctrination in cultural, subcultural and family rules, values and myths, behavior and communication patterns and other idiosyncrasies, rituals and the like, none of which is seen as just one out of many possible others but rather as aspects of the ultimate order of the world, so to speak. This image of the world evolves gradually, mostly outside a person's awareness, and becomes what he considers objective reality. In this sense, then, reality is but an individual's view of his environment and this view will, of course, determine his interactions and all his communications with this environment. As long as this view is adequate to, and in harmony with, the nature of a certain environment, and as long as this environment itself is congruent, no serious uncertainties about the world and one's place in it will arise.

But no adaptation and integration is achieved once and for all. In fact, adaptation to the contingencies of a given universe is only the smaller and easier task of the business of living, although this task, in all its manifold aspects, has received almost exclusive attention in research and literature. But the timely realization that there is constant change, that today's adaptation may lead into rigidity and alienation tomorrow, that today's achievements may be tomorrow's taboos, *this* is the major and far more difficult task facing any young person. It is the basic theme of which biological, intellectual, and emotional growth, specific successes or failures, relatedness or loneliness, the emergence of an ego image, and many other phenomena are only variations. This is where the origin of the real uncertainties is to be sought.

The assumption that what happens in one's own family happens all over the world is more or less easily corrected if childhood and adolescence allow for numerous contacts and identification with the extra-familial world. It is well known that the wider the experiential gamut in a child's life, the easier will be his final steps into young adulthood. On the other hand, if his family is a very constrained, exclusive, and isolated environment which almost places a penalty on change and growth, then the eventual breaking away from the family during and after adolescence will be difficult or even impossible. To such an adolescent the world of adulthood with its uncertainties, its entirely different duties and privileges, will appear bewildering and frightening.

So much for the uncertainties of the young adult in terms of their general denominator—i.e., the need and the ability to cope with constant change. As already suggested this need is particularly imperative when a person breaks away from home and starts to live on his own.

What then about the possible solutions? In the light of what has just been said they appear contingent upon the ability of the environment (mainly the family, but also subculture and the wider culture) to introduce this individual not only into a body of *specific* rules, but also to hand down to him the far more general and abstract rules for the *changing* of rules. This, admittedly, is a very abstract way of talking about the possibilities for solutions. However, the whole problem of the *general* rules governing change is a very difficult one, not only in family research, but equally so in biology, genetics, ecology, cybernetics, etc. In our work at the Mental Research Institute we are trying to systematize this problem. The difficulties are exasperating, but the implications of an eventual success for mental health and for psychotherapy could hardly be overrated.

If it is accepted that the uncertainties of the young adult cannot possibly be considered in isolation, it follows that the solutions, too, must be sought in the wider context of family and culture. If one begins to look at families instead of isolated individuals, a new perspective is gained and a new dimension added to old facts. This is perhaps just another way of defining a general trend in psychotherapy which is finding increasing attention: the involvement of the whole family. Family therapy is not a specific method for the solution of problems in young adulthood, but it has been found to be a promising approach for this age group as well as for others. As always in medicine, diagnostic and therapeutic criteria precede prevention. Thus, if at the present time more is known through family research and therapy about pathology than about its prevention and about normal growth and change, this will have to be accepted as a stage in the development of a wider and not only illness-oriented knowledge of human behavior.

For the healthy family is a paradox, just as culture is essentially paradoxical. The healthy family is a system which teaches its offspring to break away and thereby to destroy the system, at least in its original structure. Similarly, culture requires conformity for its survival and yet would decay and become sterile if it were not for its nonconformists. How these important paradoxes work and can be reconciled we cannot yet say, although the solution is achieved every day all over the world.

To summarize the viewpoints expressed in this paper regarding the uncertainties of the young adult: The uncertainties must be seen in the wider context in which they occur, rather than in a hypothesized interplay of intrapsychic forces only. The context is primarily the family with its 100-fold rules, norms, and idiosyncrasies. Breaking away from the family and finding one's own place in life presupposes the ability to accept and tolerate change, and this, in turn, presents a potential for solutions. For if growth and change can be made possible, either as part of the general process of education or if necessary through therapeutic intervention, the young adult will have less difficulty in facing the bewildering complexities of modern life.

PROBLEMS OF THE MIDDLE YEARS

By Klaus W. Berblinger, M.D.

In the United States there live 38 million people from 45 to 65 years of age. They are called the "middle aged" and to complicate matters, women seem to be in the majority.

By common consensus, middle-aged people are in the prime of their lives. They are the select group which have survived biologically, emotionally, economically, and socially. This means they should consider themselves more secure than the adolescent; acquire a definitive feeling of individual identity; possess adequate insurance policies to assuage their parental or connubial consciences; and hold it a privilege if they may raise children who in turn will embark on reshaping our future. Middle-aged persons have not only attained knowledge in many areas of endeavor, but are required to share their wisdom with those who are younger and less experienced. Simultaneously, they are expected to be constructive and productive in the face of actual obligations. It has been stated that middle age is the time of responsibility and, optimally, of greatest stability as far as physical and mental fitness are concerned. A less optimistic observer has defined middle age as a "reluctantly accepted position of impending decay."

Middle Age and Emotional Discomfort

Middle-aged people who come to a psychiatrist's attention seem predominantly concerned with just those aspects of their lives which should be least in jeopardy. They are preoccupied with security, health, and even death. At a time in which major changes are more likely to take place outside one's person, they may be highly sensitive to shifts denoting loss or separation; for instance, the fact that their children may leave for college, get married, venture overseas, or in any other way threaten injury to the size and cohesiveness of the family group. Coincidentally, middle-aged persons may be frantically attempting to effect for themselves just those very changes which their particular years make difficult. For example, a perpetual underachiever may consider the middle years as a last chance for changing an occupation and endeavoring to find either greater material success or a wider range of self-expression. Men and women around 50 often, and quite suddenly, terminate marital bonds although they were unsatisfactory for a long time and could have been dissolved more readily at a stage when both partners would have had an opportunity of initiating separate new lives of their own.

The middle-aged person who consults a psychiatrist usually suffers from a mixture of tension, restless anxiety, and, most of all, depression. The middle years, in psychiatric perspective, are characterized by a variety of symptoms which denote an awareness of one's actual limitations as much as they represent the individual's internal rebellion against the inevitable. This may account for the agitated, the restless, and the tense portion of the picture while the depression itself—although this may be too global and at the same time too indefinite an interpretation—suggests that in addition to declining powers and social or cultural limitations, the person begins to take notice of the horizon of his days in a conscious fashion. Depression is a state of objective as well as subjective ineffectuality that is experienced in a mood of sadness. There appears a lack or failure to anticipate, and this results in a pessimistic perspective concerning the past and the future. We also not infrequently encounter delusions of bodily decay. An unwarranted feeling of elation, or even grandiosity, may be their counterpart. However, clinical experience teaches us that those who have psychiatric difficulties for the first time and during their middle years, rarely experience that upward mood swing. Maybe if one feels all too well, one is not inclined to seek help.

The highest rate of first admissions to mental hospitals occurs between the ages of 35 to 65. If we acknowledge that schizophrenic disturbances, for instance, only occasionally become manifest past the 35 year limit for the first time, we may then conclude that, during middle age, depressions constitute the core of emotional problems in our midst. This impression is supported by the observation that the majority of patients in clinics as well as in private practice are from 40 to 60 years old.

In order to understand such predominance of middle-age depressions, one should re-examine the standard by which an individual is relegated, or assigns himself, to a particular group dependent on age alone. A striking example seems to be the artificiality of some class reunions that must rely on organized entertainment or the drawing of a "liquid curtain" in order to tolerate one's company for only a few hours or days.

SOME DEFINITIONS OF MIDDLE AGE

The pure biologist may set rather definite limits indeed, especially for women. On the other hand, the more philosophical person who values retro- and antero-spection on a continuum of introspection may refuse such biological categorization in terms of age limits alone. He exhorts us that life begins at 40, at 50, or if we behold, for example, the success stories of some of our most eminent symphony conductors, it appears that 60 years of age often represents the mere beginning. Psychologists and learning theorists describe how some of the intellectual functions increase beyond the age of 50, especially the intelligence of intellectually superior people. Others are more modest in their expectations but admit that one can still learn a good many new tricks and acquire much useful information past the age of 50.

The practicing physician, and in our particular case, the psychiatrist, is always confronted with the question of why an individual patient seeks help at a particular time. The physician must therefore familiarize himself with an individual's biological state, psychological problems, and with the social setting in which the patient has to function. These are merely some of the factors which cannot be ignored. The social scientist adds still another dimension in defining the middle years. Sociologists acknowledge that middle age begins for the manual laborer at an earlier age than for the white collar worker. Any of these assumptions are valid, and whatever the definition or delineation of the middle years may be, they indicate concurrent stresses that are biological, psychological, and social in nature.

THE PROBLEMS OF THE MIDDLE YEARS

Social

It is distressing to the psychiatrist that many health insurance policies still exempt psychological illness although probably most subscribers to such plans are somewhere within the middle age range. Thus, wherever one looks, the middle-aged person appears to be the forgotten soldier of concern. One knows he has fought his battles; one assumes he has emerged victoriously, but should he have failed, nobody but the tax assessor seems to take note of it. I believe this is part of the matrix of depressive feelings for some who have attained the age of 45.

Biological

In addition to this social oversight, if not neglect, the middle-aged person can rightfully be worried about the state of his biological functions. It is no mere accident that most of the depressed patients visit medical clinics before they come to psychiatric attention. Our culture is replete with admonitions to take care of our bodies, to consider our physical existence as ephemeral (e.g., the sales talk of some life insurance agents) and to prolong our well-being for the sake of our children rather than for ourselves. If this is true, and if we should have to forego all concern with our lives in favor of the potential survivor's, the self-esteem of the individual becomes impaired and depression ensues.

Moreover, beyond the influence of social customs, pertinent physical events actually take place in our bodies. We become aware of a definite decrease in our motor powers. A timely shift from tap dancing to tennis, from swimming to electrically propelled golf carts may scantily obscure the issue. Much has been said about the biological as well as the psychological meaning of the menopause, of decreasing sexual drive, and the cessation of a reproductive potential. But perhaps the most unequivocal reminders of "getting older" are certain changes that occur in our sensory functions. It usually begins with reading glasses or a certain inability to discriminate between the lower decibels during a symphony concert. What often is considered inattentiveness may actually be inability to participate. According to Birren's data, most of the sensory modalities decline between the ages of 55 and 65. For those who can afford and like to eat well, it may be of some comfort that taste and smell are affected least and last.

Psychological

The decrease in motor and sensory experience leads to a deficit of "input." In other words, our sources of information diminish and we have to rely on past events. Since such experiences are derived from earlier years of human communication, and being memories may have fallen victim to a certain amount of distortion, the natural biological process of aging may slant our apperception of the generally accepted norm of reality. As others continue to function without such impairment, and as the aging person may constantly be lacking in clues, a biologically determined feeling of sensory deprivation, of isolation, and a tendency to "give up" can be observed. The person who can anticipate "catabolic events" will be less prone to surrender to depression whenever signs of physical decline make their unsolicited appearance. To add to these biological certainties, there are those illnesses for which a connection between psyche and soma has been postulated. It is likely that depressive states can alter, hinder, and even permanently damage various organic functions and thus emphasize a feeling of actual decline.

THE EMPHASIS ON YOUTH

The biological determinants have equally restrictive social concomitants. The social context of our culture also predisposes the middle-aged person to depressiveness. Our culture emphasizes youth. By successive stages, a youngster is indoctrinated to be a runner, a passer, a pass receiver, and ultimately the quarterback or coach who makes the decisions. There is an obvious scarcity of well-paid coaching positions in industry, in football, as well as in our institutions of learning. The man may have learned to run, to pass, and to receive in vain and, even if the decision-making spot should become vacant, he may not be ready to assume such responsibility. We encounter as many depressions at that situational level where one was passed over for promotion, as we see in those who have reached the chairmanship.

It is difficult to discern whether our image-makers' neglect of the middle-aged is the result of a general orientation or due to the relative ease with which one can portray the unspoiled and the young. For instance, we may look at two scantily clad kids offering each other a soft drink across the tennis net. The male seems to outlast the female contemporary and rates a full page advertisement as a "man of distinction." However, soon afterward, middle-aged men, as well as women, disappear from the scene of public acknowledgment, save for the gossip columns. They reappear just before the gate is closing under the caption, "how we retired to Florida at 65 on $150 a month."

If we proceed from fancy to fact, there is no escape from the realization that most employers prefer men below 40 and women of beauty as much as of experience. The argument here is not whether such overemphasis on youth is justified, but rather how it must affect the ones who no longer qualify for the epitaphs of youth, beauty, or unlimited strength. One may assume that many of the more insidious forms of middle age depressions constitute the direct outgrowth of an actual dilemma which tells you, on the one hand, that you should be young and, on the other, won't let you ignore the fact that you are 40 or over.

The transition from social to psychological unpreparedness for an increase in years and for the decrease in biological capacity may be inherent in our educational system. Our society is achievement oriented, and at no level of the learning process or in any institution of learning, where one gathers the samples, have we been taught to accept failure. No wonder that those who can no longer ride the crest of expectation and ambition will react with increasing discomfort.

One might expect that a mature and insightful person is at least aware of the social dilemma. He surely would have witnessed it over and over in others. However, first of all, he may not always have been conscious of his shifting point of observation. He may have viewed the middle-aged person from the perspective of youth until he personally felt confronted by the biological and psychological dilemma of getting older. Furthermore, up to this time, he may have thought that he could escape or compensate for middle age, especially if he has been in spectacular physical and mental health before. Yet, one often notes that just such persons are prone to become more acutely and severely depressed by comparison with individuals who have been at least cognizant of possible breaking points before and, therefore, had the advantage of a certain measure of insight. If such has not been the case, some middle-aged persons who exhibit depressive symptomatology will appear victims of their own interpretation of the demands which the surroundings make. In other words, their own value systems, their ideals, the way in which they insist upon success and self-realization seem in acute conflict with each other. I do not intend to play down the importance of cultural pressures, but it is my conviction that the majority of middle age depressions are a mixture of irreconciled value systems and the assessment of self-realization and achievement at crucial stages of social or biological loss. A mother may become upset at the time of her daughter's adolescence, not so much because the daughter strays from the beaten path, but because the mother is placed unequivocally in the position of the matron and simultaneously may unconsciously share the daughter's conflicts in becoming a mature woman. Analogous constellations arise about the infirmities or the death of parents, ambivalent feelings about one's employer, and the acknowledgment of one's own omissions or commissions. This means that the middle years stress one's preconceived notions about oneself, one's naive reliance on physical resources, and the picture that one feels coerced to portray to one's contemporaries. The certainty of previous convictions will be put to a crucial test. Self-pity leads to retreat, rigidity of beliefs to projection and denial, exaggerated flexibility—or even submissiveness—to evasion or depression. The more any of these time-honored defenses predominate and unilaterally defy reality, the greater may be the liability for actual psychiatric illness.

POSSIBLE SOLUTIONS

Psychiatric Treatment: A few remarks may be in order concerning the treatment of depressive illness during the middle years.

It is noteworthy that the great progress made in psychiatry during the last half of this century, and also much of the research effort expended, has concerned the exploration of infancy, adolescence, and, of late, geriatric psychiatry. It seems as if research concerning the middle years has been relegated to the other behavioral disciplines. Certainly, general medicine makes every attempt to prevent aging from an organic point of view, and sociologists have long recognized the problems that confront the middle-aged. On the other hand, there are also many new and refined treatment modalities for middle-aged people in the field of psychiatry. These may not be specific for this age group alone but are applicable in a selective way.

I am thinking here of the various psychotherapies, group and individual, supportive and uncovering, and of Adolf Meyer's concept of "distributive analysis." In addition, there are a number of physical therapies. It is probably correct to state that the electroconvulsive treatment for the middle-aged group of patients is markedly on the decline, having been replaced by psychopharmacological approaches which are often carried out by non-psychiatrists. For the psychiatrist, the general practitioner, and nonpsychiatric specialist, as well as for workers in the paramedical fields, it should be stated that the actual psychiatric incapacitation during the middle years is often short in duration and therefore one of the more rewarding treatment experiences for patient and physician alike.

Prevention

However, the psychological prevention of depression during the middle years is dependent on the perceptiveness of all those who customarily have first-hand contact with persons between 45 and 65. One could mention employers, clergymen, agency workers, and many others who meet a prospective employee, client, or patient and then discover a tendency toward depression, despondency, or even self-destructive behavior. Not every middle-aged person who is mildly depressed must consult a psychiatrist. The psychiatrist in turn should never aid and abet in obscuring the relative validity of the patient's conflicts in living. Psychotherapy with the middle aged means acknowledging realistic stress, ameliorating the overload, and helping the patient to find *actual* solutions to current problems rather than encouraging him to deal with *actual* situations in an *obsolete* way.

The middle years are characterized by the interrelatedness of unavoidable biological changes, social circumstances and their effect upon the psychological state of the individual. From the psychiatrist's point of view, emphasis should be placed on focal conflict and team work whenever a patient has difficulty in saying good-by to youth.

PERSPECTIVES FOR LEISURE AND RETIREMENT

By Marjorie Fiske Lowenthal

Since the turn of the century the proportion of elderly people in the United States has more than doubled; at the same time the proportion employed has consistently dwindled, so that today two-thirds of the men 65 and over and nearly 90 per cent of the women are "at leisure." Nearly one-tenth of our population, then, is caught up in a highly conflicted social situation, victims of two sets of ambiguities which reinforce each other. First, we have a youth-oriented society whose admonitions to its elders waver between "stay young" and "grow old gracefully" (meaning "get out of our way"). If they do get out of the way, they soon run afoul of sharp ambivalences in a second sphere, namely, toward the uses of time, ambivalences expressed at the one extreme by the Protestant Ethic and at the other by a kind of consumer hedonism. Our conflicts about aging, then, are confounded by our conflicts about leisure.

Mixed feelings about aging and the aged have no doubt prevailed for as long as man has been aware of the inevitability of death. The Greeks were by no means in agreement on the subject: Homer exalted Nestor in the *Iliad;* Aristotle, on the other hand, drew a particularly negative picture of elderly men in his *Rhetoric,* calling them cynical, small-minded, too fond of themselves, loquacious about the past, and querulous. Plato's views were mainly optimistic (e.g., Cephalous in *The Republic*). At the same time, he seemed to recognize that reality was far from ideal, for in the *Laws* he found it necessary to prescribe to the young about their attitudes toward the old, and prescribe to the old about fitting behavior for their stage in life.[1]

Shakespeare took a somewhat dimmer view, as expressed in the last stage of his seven ages of man, but this is somewhat mitigated in the spiritual development of *King Lear* and the romantic image of Prospero in *The Tempest.*

The nineteenth century poets, at least those who survived to old age, were—true to the general optimism of their age—more sanguine, Browning insisting that "the best is yet to be" and Longfellow (Morituri Salutamus) reciting the achievements of old men from Sophocles to Goethe, concluded with:

---

[1] Maria S. Haynes: The supposedly golden age for the aged in ancient greece (a study of literary concepts of old age). Gerontologist 2 (2): 1962.

For age is opportunity no less
Than youth itself, tho' in another dress
And as the evening twilight fades away
The sky is filled with stars invisible by day.

Our contemporary poets take a more tragic view of aging, as epitomized by T. S. Eliot in sections of his "Four Quartets," for example.

In antiquity, the idea of leisure was considerably less controversial than that of aging: Greek society was firmly grounded on the principle of slavery, the rationale of which was to release the upper classes for service to the state and for self-cultivation. The social structure of the Middle Ages perpetuated this principle, and it is not until the 16th and 17th centuries that we find the uses of leisure being an object of intellectual debate. The French philosopher Montaigne, a firm believer in the need of the individual to "escape" in what time he had free from work and other necessities of life, disagreed with his countryman and colleague of half a century later, Pascal, who felt that leisure should be used for the cultivation of the soul. This debate has flourished ever since, becoming especially vigorous in 18th century England, with the simultaneous rise of the middle classes and of the mass media.[2] That the issue is not yet resolved is readily apparent in our discomfiture over the modern mass media or over such hedonistically touted ventures for the aged as are represented by the retirement community devastatingly profiled in *The New Yorker*.[3]

And there is no doubt that in a few years to come the problem of the uses of time of people over 65 will become accentuated, as medical and economic advances provide them with more energy and freedom. Nor is there reason to believe that mental or emotional impairment is much more widespread among the elderly than among the young. At least one group of epidemiologists[4] report evidence for a decline in rate of mental disorder after age 70, and a number of psychiatrists and psychoanalysts adhere to the theory that the neuroses and some psychoses tend to burn themselves out with age. And the fact remains that fewer than one per cent of our aged are in mental hospitals, and about half of these have grown old there. As to the psychiatric status of the elderly in the community at large, in our Langley Porter study of San Francisco aged, in which we heavily over-weighted the sample of the very old, we found only 10 per cent moderately impaired and 5 per cent severely impaired. While a 15 per cent rate of

[2]Marjorie Fiske and Leo Lowenthal: The Debate Over Art and Popular Culture: English Eighteenth Century as a Case Study. *In* Leo Lowenthal, Literature, Popular Culture and Society. Englewood Cliffs, N. J., Prentice Hall, 1961 (paperback).

[3]*The New Yorker*, April 4, 1964.

[4]Leighton, Dorothea, C., et al.: The Character of Danger. New York, Basic Books, 1963.

psychiatric impairment may seem high, it is nevertheless about the same as that reported for younger groups in a recent mental health survey in New York City.[5]

In short, when we confront the problems of leisure and retirement, we are focusing on a very large segment of our society, one which is not much worse off mentally and emotionally than the rest of us and one which, though now about as likely to be suffering from disabling chronic physical illness as not, can be expected to become increasingly more vigorous physically as medical advances are made.

Unlike other developmental stages of life, for which social norms and expectations are fairly clear, this segment of our population moves—or is shoved—into a social limbo at the other end of which looms death. As some of you may know, there is now a controversy raging in gerontological circles regarding whether this movement is "good" or "bad" from the standpoint of the individual, goodness or badness being measured in terms of morale, life satisfaction, or mental health. This withdrawal, voluntary or involuntary, has been labeled "disengagement," and the initial formulation of a theory that disengagement is not incompatible with high morale came from University of Chicago sociologist Elaine Cumming and psychologist William Henry. This theory, however, has as yet by no means offset the activity theory which preceded it and which exhorted the elderly citizen to "get out and mix."

Our own work suggests that neither Montaigne's escape theory, Cumming and Henry's disengagement theory, nor the activity theory can be applied across the board. Later I shall cite some support for Pascal's theory, though certainly not to advocate it as a universal panacea, and offer a practical suggestion as one of many possible "potentials for solution." But first I should like to report briefly on what we have learned about interaction, isolation, disengagement, and escape. Our findings can be summarized within the framework of five studies, all based on 534 psychiatrically hospitalized elderly persons and 600 community-resident aged. The first study examined the problem of lifelong extreme isolation; the second explored the potentially isolation-producing antecedents of mental illness in old age; the third analyzed the sequence in the development of three dominant characteristics of the hospitalized (physical illness, isolation, and mental symptoms); the fourth, the relation between isolation and morale; and the fifth compares the morale of voluntary and involuntary disengagers and also examines their inclination to "escape" via the mass media.

---

[5]Thomas A. Langner and Stanley T. Michael: Life Stress and Mental Health. New York, The Free Press of Glencoe, 1963.

1. EXTREME, LIFELONG ISOLATION

In the course of analyzing our 1200 elderly persons, we found small groups in both the community and hospital samples who have been extreme isolates all of their lives. They are people who say: "I'm a lone wolf, I strictly mind my own business—that covers it," or "I've been alone all my life, never had any friends, always went alone," or I was always a tramp, nobody travelled with me; I went alone." Extreme isolates tended to be persons from the lowest rung of the socioeconomic ladder. But we found no evidence that their lifelong social deviance (which, of course, might be culturally defined as mental illness in itself) is at all conducive to hospitalization for mental disorder in old age, nor is there evidence of low morale among the isolates—in fact, several of them ranked higher on our morale measures than did persons who reported high levels of social interaction. And unlike the interactors, they rarely reported being lonely. Having been thoroughly disengaged all their lives, the aging process in fact seems much smoother for them than for the highly involved.

2. ISOLATION-PRODUCING SITUATIONS AS ANTECEDENTS OF PSYCHOLOGICAL MALADJUSTMENT IN OLD AGE

But what about the less dramatic forms of isolation? Is there evidence that a rather marginal social existence is conducive to isolation and mental illness in old age? Since we could not directly measure the social interaction of our patients at various stages of their lifespan, we had to rely on indirect measures. By arranging all the major events and circumstances of the lives of our psychiatrically ill hospitalized sample onto a life history schedule, we were able to pinpoint a group of potentially isolation-producing circumstances, such as loss of a parent in childhood, early psychological problems or interpersonal conflicts, sporadic employment, and relatives with psychiatric illness. What we learned was that such circumstances have no bearing on the current isolation of the patient.

We also discovered, however, that these various symptoms of earlier life problems, though unrelated to current isolation, are far more frequently found among elderly patients suffering from psychogenic disorders such as depression or paranoia than among those suffering from organic disorder. Our conclusion is that these lifelong problems—while not necessarily conducive to isolation—are related to late-developing depression, paranoia, or alcoholism. It is not, in short, the isolation consequent upon these life stresses, but the stresses themselves which are decisive. But we should bear in mind that people who suffer from psychogenic (or functional) disorder represent only a small proportion of those who require hospitalization for psychiatric disorder in old age. Most elderly first admissions suffer from organic brain damage, and for them these earlier life stresses seem to be of little account. Our life history analysis of these organically brain-damaged patients did indicate, however, that they had very often been physically ill prior to the development of their psychiatric symptoms. Could it be that their isolation resulted from the physical problem and that the isolation was in turn followed by psychiatric problems?

3. PHYSICAL ILLNESS—ISOLATION—PSYCHIATRIC SYMPTOMS

Using the same life history schedules, we then analyzed the sequence of physical, psychiatric, and social developments preceding admission to the psychiatric ward. The results lend no support to a hypothesis that isolation following physical illness is conducive to the development of psychiatric disorder. In fact, the physically ill were frequently less isolated than the physically well. Adding to this our previous finding that potentially isolation-conducive early stresses and symptoms are not correlated with degree of current isolation, our conclusion, then, was that the severe isolation characterizing those elderly people who eventually find their way to a psychiatric ward is more likely to be a consequence than a cause of their mental illness.

Thus far, then, we have learned that we cannot blame isolation for the development of extreme maladjustment in old age. How about the relationship between isolation and a less extreme form of maladjustment—low morale? We have explored this problem in two ways. First, looking at our total group of 1200, we have analyzed the relationship between level of social interaction and morale; second, looking at just the community aged, we have compared the engaged with the disengaged and the voluntary with the involuntary disengagers.

4. ISOLATION AND MORALE

We asked our subjects several questions relating to mood and satisfaction with life. Analysis of the answers to these questions indicated three dimensions of morale, which we have called depression, irritability, and the will to live. On all of these dimensions, those who were most active socially received higher scores than those who were less active, the discrepancy being by far the most marked in the depression dimension. At first glance, this seems to be clear vindication of the activist, or "get out and mix," theory of aging. Obviously, for many elderly people, this is sound advice. On the other hand—and this is the old problem of whether you see the glass as half empty or half full—over a third of those reporting very little social interaction were *not* depressed, and about two-thirds of them ranked high on the other two dimensions of morale. Eager to learn more about the dynamics of this seemingly ambiguous relationship between social interaction and morale, we took advantage of the fact that we were studying these people through time. In the course of our two year follow-up of the community sample, we were able to pinpoint two groups, those who had manifested some social withdrawal during that time and those who had not.

5. Voluntary vs. Involuntary Disengagement

Our findings in regard to level of social interaction and morale were confirmed when we compared the morale of those who report a decline in social contact with that of those who do not. Among those who had not withdrawn, somewhat over half, or 52 per cent, ranked fairly high on morale measures, but at the same time as many as 42 per cent of those who had withdrawn ranked equally high. Social withdrawal, then, is not necessarily conducive to low morale. The obverse of these figures, however, tells us something else: 48 per cent of the engaged and 58 per cent of the disengaged had low morale. Clearly neither the disengagement theory nor the interaction theory tells the whole story. We therefore decided to look into the problem more closely—with special attention to the engaged with low morale and the disengaged with high morale. To do this, those people in the community sample who reported a decrease in social interaction over a two year period were divided between those whose social withdrawal was most likely the result of forces beyond their control and those whose withdrawal was apparently of their own volition. In the forced-withdrawal group are those persons who had been compulsorily retired or who had suffered widowhood up to seven years before the reported decrease in social interaction, or who had been physically ill or disabled within a three year period. The voluntarily disengaged consist of those who reported a decrease in interaction but who were not subject to any of these pressures. Next, those who had not withdrawn were divided in the same way—that is to say, between those who had such pressures and those who did not. This procedure delineated four groups which we have labeled as follows:

1. The involuntarily disengaged (pressures and withdrawal).
2. The voluntarily disengaged (withdrawal, no pressures).
3. The unafflicted engaged (no withdrawal, no pressures).
4. The afflicted engaged (no withdrawal, pressures).

The involuntary disengagers—those who had withdrawn as a result of pressures—consistently ranked lowest on all of the morale clusters, while the unafflicted engaged—those who had not withdrawn and who had not suffered widowhood, retirement, or illness—consistently ranked highest. The afflicted engaged had relatively low morale, resembling the afflicted disengaged, while the voluntarily disengaged had fairly high morale, closely resembling the unafflicted engaged. These findings suggest that both disengagement theory and activist theory are applicable—a person can disengage and maintain morale if the disengagement is voluntary, and he has even higher morale if he hasn't disengaged at all. But if a person has experienced any of the major stresses of aging—retirement, widowhood, or physical illness —he tends to have low morale whether socially withdrawn or not, suggesting that it is these stresses themselves rather than the potentially consequent isolation which results in low morale. It will be recalled that we found similar results in studying the antecedents of mental illness in old age: It was the antecedents themselves rather than any intervening isolation that was decisive.

What we see here is that some people have a need to withdraw as they grow older and by and large (but not always) have the inner resources to, nevertheless, live satisfying lives. Others are forced to withdraw through retirement or other exigencies of the aging process such as physical illness or widowhood, and while some of them (about one-fifth) manage to maintain a satisfying equilibrium, the majority do not.

And what are they doing with their time, these elderly people who have voluntarily or involuntarily withdrawn from social relationships? Studies of the uses of leisure at various ages indicate that people past retirement age spend somewhat more time viewing television or listening to the radio or in other solitary or semisolitary pursuits, and our own studies show, as was to be expected, that retired people spend more time on these activities than do older working people. For example, about 30 per cent of the retired people watch television three or more hours a day compared with about half that many among the working elderly. These differences persist in radio and reading time and in other nonsocial pursuits, but they are by no means sufficient to account for the use of that extra 40 hours a week or more which are at the disposal of the retired.

Some hint of what may be transpiring is found in our comparison of voluntary and involuntary disengagers. The voluntary disengagers, you will recall, are persons who have recently reduced their social activity, presumably without any external pressure for doing so. The involuntary disengagers are those who have reduced their social activity as a result of ill health, retirement, or widowhood (or all three). Did both of these groups simply then spend more time on the mass media? Surprisingly, the answer is quite different for the two of them: During the period when they withdrew from social contacts, the voluntary disengagers also began to spend *less* time with the mass media, while the involuntary disengagers spent more time with them than ever. At the same time we know that about two-thirds of our voluntary disengagers have relatively high morale, and conversely about four-fifths of our involuntary disengagers have low morale. In other words, if you have voluntarily withdrawn from social activities you maintain high morale without the need to "escape" through additional exposure to the mass media. If you have involuntarily disengaged you seek such solace but do not necessarily find it.

For interpretation of these findings we are examining detailed life histories of a number of these people. One of our tentative conclusions is that, for many older people, escape or distraction (as recommended, for example, by Montaigne) is not conducive to life satisfaction in old age. Rather, it would almost seem as though Pascal's advice is followed, that men should "reflect on what they are, whence they came, and whither they go." Dr. Robert Butler, a research psychiatrist who has spent considerable time with old people both as patients and as research subjects, has proferred the idea of the "life review" as a developmental phase in the aging process. "The life review is not simply to be viewed as looking back, but looking back as set in motion by looking forward to death and potentially proceeding toward personality reorganization."[6] Anthropologists Margaret Clark and Barbara Anderson, analyzing life history materials from our protocols at Langley Porter, are postulating a theory of successful aging which elaborates on the importance of re-evaluation of one's past and current life, resulting, for the lucky ones at least, in a new synthesis. Our most satisfied elderly people have been able to discard some of the instrumental values of our society and find a new contentment in "just being." As one of our very elderly women expressed it, "I grow more like myself every year."

Our better educated oldsters have an easier time in mastering this developmental phase than do their less privileged peers, but the tendency is noticeable in all socioeconomic groups: the former unskilled worker who writes essays, for example; the housewife who writes memoirs or the letter-writing retired tailor. We think these people are telling us something important. They have passed through the postretirement frustration at being useless to a groping concern with enduring values. They are not seeking escape in their leisure, but wisdom. In their own ways, they are telling us how the postretirement void can be filled, what kinds of roles older people can play in our society, and they are dong it without any help from the larger society which has presented them with no guidelines and no expectations. They are themselves, in short, suggesting "potentials for solution"; they are saying that not all of our older people want to play out their

---

[6]Robert N. Butler: Psychiatry 26: 65-76, 1963.

later years romping in the sun. Some have the inner resources to work out their own salvation, in Pascal's terms.

Their directives to the larger society seem clear: We need standards, values, norms for growing old just as we need them for growing up. And who is in a better position to formulate such standards and values than older people themselves? To encourage this spontaneous urge of many older people to move into a creative, ruminative, value-oriented phase, I believe (and now I come to my favorite "potential for solution") that we need serious educational institutions run for (and by) older people, institutions which acknowledge the fact that their needs are qualitatively different from the instrumental goals of younger people in our society. Such institutions might consist of state-or foundation-supported high schools and colleges — with full accreditation, granting diplomas and degrees — with curricula heavily emphasizing history, philosophy, comparative religion, and the social sciences—for persons in their sixties and seventies. You might interpolate that such facilities abound in the various facets of the adult education movement throughout the country. Theoretically, they do, but by and large older people do not participate to any great extent because, I suspect, they are geared to the needs of their younger participants who are still very much in the instrumental phase of development. While in general I do not favor segregation on the basis of age, I am convinced that the developmental needs of older adults differ at least as much from those of younger adults as those of the high school student differ from those of the fourth grader. The educational process is facilitated in the presence of one's peers. Therefore, it seems to me that we should design educational facilities specifically for the aged.

Not only would our older students then be able to retain a sense of continuing development which is important to many of them, but eventually society would benefit by having a pool of wise elders to help those behind them to go through the "initiation rites" of aging with dignity and serenity. In reaching out, away from themselves and toward enduring values they would not only work toward the attainment of that integrity which Erik Erikson postulates as the main task of later maturity,[7] but they could not help but produce a stabilizing effect on the increasingly frenetic world about them. We must, in short, provide an opportunity to re-engage for those who wish to do so.

[7]Identity and the Life Cycle, Psychological Issues, Monograph No. 1, New York, International Universities Press, 1959.

PEOPLE AS INDIVIDUALS: THEIR BIOLOGICAL AND SOCIAL LIMITS AND POSSIBILITIES—A COLLOQUIUM

MODERATOR'S INTRODUCTION

By CHAUNCEY D. LEAKE, PH.D.

The topic, "People as Individuals: Their Biological and Social Limits and Possibilities," at once brings into clear focus the interrelation of social considerations and of individual factors. We here consider one of the most important, ancient, and difficult problems relating to the maintenance of social and individual mental health: How can individuals maintain their intellectual and emotional freedom while at the same time preserving the benefits of participating in a social unity.

A basic biological problem confronts us here, in respect to the significance of the organizational level of living material with which we are concerned. This problem was first clearly indicated by Rudolph Virchow in 1847, when he founded his great journal to establish pathology as a worthy science. The cell theory had just come along, and Virchow was impressed with the possibility of studying disease processes at a cellular level. For centuries, of course, disease had been appreciated at an individual level, and from the 16th century on there had been increasing recognition of the importance of disease factors at organ and tissue levels. Virchow boldly stated, however, that he intended to study disease from cells to societies. We have not caught up with him yet. Meanwhile, however, we have gone beyond his point of view. At one end of the organizational scale we realize that cells are actually not the units of living material, but that there are many complex subcellular organizational factors, and, at the other, we go beyond societies to consider ecological milieus.

Two prime problems emerge from these considerations. (1) We do not yet understand the coordinating factors that involve living processes at any particular organizational level, and (2) we seldom appreciate the dangers of attempting to jump from findings and conclusions at one level of biological organization to another.

These matters are important in considering the relations of individuals to their social environment. Most of us understand pretty well what we are individually as ourselves. We blithely think that other people are quite like us and that therefore (an obvious fallacy) their social behavior should be

127

quite as it is with ourselves as individuals. A moment's reflection indicates how wrong it is to make this jump. The individuals comprising a mob may individually be very decent people. The mob, however, may act in a way beyond the capacity of one individual.

Here we consider people as individuals. This focuses upon the individual level of biological organization and brings into focus mental health as it applies to each separate and distinct individual.

One of the important aspects of this matter is the increasing recognition of the extraordinary differences that there are between us, not only with respect to our personal appearance, so that we can recognize each other as individuals, but actually in our genetic makeup, our chemical constitution, and our differences in coordinatable ability. Mental health comprises the satisfactory and satisfying adaptation of each individual, not only to himself or herself, but to all others who may be around, and to the environmental milieu in general.

We have a distinguished panel. It includes Doctor Kenneth M. Colby, Doctor William R. Dennes, Sir John C. Eccles, and Doctor Ralph W. Gerard. For the purpose of our discussion, we will hear from each of the members of the panel regarding mental health in people, considering people as individuals with respect to their limits and possibilities. This is a wide open field.

PANEL PRESENTATION

SIR JOHN ECCLES, M.D., F.R.S., RALPH M. GERARD, M.D.,
KENNETH MARK COLBY, M.D., WILLIAM R. DENNES, D. PHIL.

SIR JOHN C. ECCLES, M.D., F.R.S.

I am going to talk on the subject "What is an Individual?" We have this symposium on "People as Individuals," and to me the key problem arises from the question "What is an individual?" There is only one way to approach this problem, or only one valid way, shall I say, and that consists of looking at yourself. I am going to base my account in the first instance on my own experience, so it will be initially a purely personal and egocentric account. I know that it is an unfashionable method, but never mind; perhaps it may be more interesting because unfashionable—who wants to go just with the stream? What I will call methodological solipsism is in essence the outlook on this problem that I have had since my adolescence —always attempting to face up to the problem of trying to discover what I am. This is to me the only worthwhile problem in the world; but, of course, I am not suggesting that I restrict my interest just to myself as an individual. Naturally, I extend it to all other people, and I recognize them as being individuals just as I am. However, for a start, I will just talk about myself, and you can translate it for yourself as I go along.

My conscious experience is all that is given to me in my effort to understand not only myself but the world. As a scientist I build my science upon what I experience in certain very particular circumstances, namely during experiments and in all the discussions and ideas that arise therefrom. I come to know this world and I try to understand it as a scientist entirely through my perceptual experiences, my conscious experiences. It is only as a conscious individual that one can operate effectively at all, and I submit that this is true of all other human activities that are worthwhile and for other human beings when indulging in activities that are worthwhile. Now, when I talk of my conscious experiences, I do not mean only my immediate perceptual experiences. I can look around this room now and can see all of you sitting on seats wearing your various colors and arranged in rows and illuminated by the lights—and all that kind of thing; and I can even hear myself talking. No, these are not all that I mean. I mean, in addition, all my experiences that can be recalled in memory and so re-experienced;

this is what gives me, in fact, the concept that I am something more than just a transient experience—an individual is much more than that.

One has an existence in time strung along by memory right back into one's past and also projected into some future which you can anticipate with hope or foreboding. We must necessarily take ourselves into this whole picture in space and time. I recognize my unity and identity through-out all the past vicissitudes, and I want you to think of yourself as an individual and everybody else here as individuals in this category. It is memory that gives me that continuity of inner experience, which is inter-rupted in sleep and for other more unpleasant reasons, but we pick it up again. If you never remembered anything about what happened before you went to sleep, you would never have this concept of a self or indi-vidual. Is it not a curious experience that we always wake up in the morning and slowly come around and recognize that we are in just the same room and all the rest of the environment as when we lost conscious-ness the night before? We take it for granted. It is the same self, then, that wakes to another stream of consciousness for another waiting day. Now, not only do we have memory of events, but we have all the conscious texture of imagery and ideas, of desire and love and fear and other emo-tional feelings. All these much more subtle experiences, I assume, are yours as well as mine. They characterize our waking life; but, also, when asleep we have dreams and all kinds of other states such as daydreaming and hallucinatory states and all the rest of it. All of this is part of our conscious experience, the whole assemblage throughout our lives having contributed to the formation of ourselves—of each of us as an individual. It is solely from my perceptual experiences that I have the moment-to-moment impression of my surroundings. I am speaking now of my immediate perceptual experiences interpreted on the basis of all the immense educa-tional effort that has gone into the past. Without knowing it we are learn-ing all the time how to interpret experiences of new and subtle kinds from babyhood onward; and, even now, you would have a whole set of new experience if you suddenly decided, for example, to learn skiing. You have to learn how to interpret a whole lot of new sensory information from muscles, joints, and the vestibular apparatus and to correlate these with speed and accuracy with visual information so that you adapt perfectly and become the accomplished skier. Now, this continuous process of learning is what gives us a knowledge of the world and our relationship to it. This knowledge is so extraordinarily sophisticated and complete that we can find our way around in the world, dodging traffic and living through all manner of hazardous situations; yet, we do it with complete aplomb. We have learned how to interpret the total inflow of information, and we are not conscious that it is any problem at all. You may become conscious of the problem, though, when somebody else is driving in traffic and they are not so good at it and their reaction time is slow. That puts you into the position of realizing what a complex procedure it really is.

But on the whole, we take it all for granted, and you're apt so often to think that, as expressed in naive realism, you are given a direct and immediate experience of everything in your surroundings; that in some mysterious manner your perceptions give you a direct and exact knowledge of things and events in the external world. On the contrary, we neurophysiologists know that all our information about the world, everything that we have ever learned about it, is fed into our brains by sense organs firing in a coded pattern along millions of nerve channels. It is much more complicated than a TV set—even than color TV. The colors we think we see with our eyes come to our brain merely as a coded pattern of impulses in the optic nerves. It is a Morse code of dots only in each individual optic nerve fiber. Because of the tremendous machine that is our brain, all this coded information is integrated into a colored picture in a way that no physiologist understands.

I want you to realize how little we know. We can trace the information up to the brain and perhaps one synaptic relay beyond, but in the ten thousand million neurons beyond that we can pick up transient flashes of integrated activity in the brain—say one cell fired from hearing, from vision and, perhaps, from a muscle movement and so on. There are ten thousand million cells there, and altogether neurophysiologists have looked at a few thousand from this point of view. I want to impress you with how little we do know about brain activity.

This statement leads me to the dogmatic assertions often made that science, and neurophysiology in particular, makes it impossible to believe in free will. I believe, implicitly, in free will, and I don't care that you can't explain it by present-day science. To me, and I suggest also to you, it is a direct experience, and I ask you always to believe your direct experiences even if they are contrary to the dictates of the fashionable science of the time. Fashionable science is transitory. For example, the deterministic physics of the last centuries is now rejected except as an approximation. We neurophysiologists are, as yet, so terribly primitive in our understanding that we do know only an extremely minute fraction of what is going on in a human brain in the most simple actions or experiences. So, we do not know how I can move my finger if I wish. We can tell you all the pathways from the brain outward. For example, we can tell of impulses down the pyramidal tract to the motoneurons that in turn act on the muscles, but no one can give an account of even the immediately preceding events that cause the pyramidal cells to fire impulses. All that went on before that is completely unknown. So, let's not dramatize what science teaches about the determinism of the neuronal mechanisms concerned in voluntary movement.

Now I will give you a general principle that arises from the great mass of experiments and observations on the brain and, perhaps, has not yet been formulated very rigorously. It is that, with every perceptual experience, every memory, every conscious experience of any kind that we have there is some specific pattern in space and time being played out in the neuronal network of our brain. We roughly can see evidence for this in investigations on the electrical waves from the cerebral cortex which display variations in patterns with different sensory inputs, and we can pick up the responses of the individual cells; but no one has made any approach to appreciating what the pattern could be that is concerned in even the simplest experience. Yet this general principle is, I think, accepted by all neurophysiologists and, I hope, by all psychologists, namely that there appears to be for each experience a unique patterned activity in the neuronal network and that the complexity of the brain is sufficient to allow us to make this statement. Even if you have millions of memories and experiences already stored in your brain, you will still have the potentiality in your brain for an untold tremendous amount of new specific patterns. It isn't as if your brain could get overloaded with so much memory that it can't take in anymore. However, it is very important to reject a lot of memories. I think one of the most important things you can do is to forget. Forgetting is just as important as memorizing, just as in the detailed mechanism of brain action inhibition is as important as excitation.

As I go along in developing my story, I think you will understand that it is going to be done by just a little illumination here and there and a lot for you to fill in. We have subjective experiences, conscious experiences as a consequence of neuronal actions in our brains, and these experiences are all private in the first instance. For any observed event you can check your experiences with those of other observers and say, for example, that he lifted that object and then put it back again. You are all well aware that you can always have this exchange of experience with others. We learn to reject solipsism in this way because we find other people have the same experiences as ours and hence presumably are like us. But this is not always true. Colorvision is an example of how color perception can go wrong so that we have a group of people who can't match colors the way the majority do. We label those people as color blind, which is quite a simple way of solving the problem of differences in perception. We don't doubt the validity of color perception just because of the differences between individuals. The same solution occurs in our concept of hallucinations. For example, when people take hallucinogenic drugs that give them experiences that we can't see, we say they have hallucinations.

We discover this similarity with others, not only in perceptual experiences, as I have described, but also with all our inner experiences and feelings. We discover that others have experiences like ours, such as dreams for example. You are familiar with all the talking that goes on about dreams and our feeling that we've had this too. But I want you also to consider such inner experiences as joy or anguish or aesthetic delight. Think how hard it is to describe to anybody what your experiences are when you are being deeply moved by music, especially if you are musically educated. How can you find words adequate to describe the deep and intense rapture that you may feel. Artists are attempting this highly sophisticated task in literature and in plastic art and all other artistic activities. For example, in literature the author is communicating to us the inner experiences of the characters that he creates, and we read literature and become sophisticated in an understanding of other individuals by virtue of a knowledge of this world of literature. In this way we learn to share experiences with the creative artist and with other people like ourselves who are enjoying and appreciating artistic creation. Hence, in this way I come to believe that this world is inhabited by other selves like myself because I can tune into them in these more sophisticated ways of communication in language and in art. Thus, it is that I come to recognize not only my own egocentric position of a self associated with a body that I can experience but that other people are similar. They, in varying dergees, have comparable bodies, comparable reactions, comparable joys and appreciations that I can learn about by talking to them and in more subtle ways of communication.

Why are you all here today to listen to this forum? Presumably, you believe there is something in it—you believe there are individuals. In line with all that I have said, you believe that the purely solipsistic position becomes untenable when living as we all do in society with our fellow men; but, in the first place, I want you to appreciate that your knowledge of society is derived from your own inner experiences as an existing self—as an individual—and that society is made up of individuals like yourselves. It is not some great immaterial conglommeration, but it is an immense diversity of living, appreciating beings such as you are. Now it is this philosophy of life, of individuals, that I wanted specifically to present to you today, and I tried at the same time to build it up upon what we do know about brains and perceptual experiences and inner experiences. I have also tried to tell you how little we do know. I think it is very important for philosophers to realize that scientific knowledge in physiology is still in a very primitive state. Although we can do magnificent things in lots of ways, when it comes down to the very essence or nature of experiences we can tell you nothing at all. We cannot tell you how the assumed patterns of activity in the neuronal network ever give rise to consciousness, nor can we tell how, when I make a decision to move something or to do anything, I can do it. We have no knowledge of how thought can be expressed in action, yet we know it must be so.

I admit that this is a very sketchy philosophy that I have presented to you, but believe that it can be extended to encompass all experience and all knowledge. I want to warn you against philosophies that reject much of experience as being inadmissable for the purpose of building a science or a philosophy. You have to account for all experience though you may explain it differently and weigh it differently. It is for this reason that I warn you against all behavioral philosophies. The behavioral investigation of man is all right up to a point. It's useful to know how input relates to output. It's good for experimenting and providing statistical data, but you must remember that it is rejecting the greater part of the actual nature and experience of the individual. We know that individuals are not just behaving units because we can look within ourselves and see our own conscious individuality. So, I warn you against the philosophies that exclusively claim to build upon the nature of man as a behaving being, as some computer or cybernetic or robot man. The primary data upon which I build everything, even as a scientist, is myself as a conscious being and ultimately as a spiritual being. There is a great unknown mystery in each of us as an individual. By virtue of our brains and the tremendous wealth of input from receptor organs and the effector organs that our brains operate through, we receive from this world and we give to this world as individuals, but we, in a sense, have conscious existences as spiritual beings apart from this world. My final summing up is that we must look at ourselves primarily from the inside. It is a privileged position that each of us has in this world, and we must not forego that privilege.

Dr. Leake: Sir John confided in me that he is really a neo-Cartesian, and I can see that he is following Descartes' 17th century dictum: "I think, therefore, I am."

Individuals as people or people as individuals, we are obviously limited by our genes. There is the possibility within us, of course, that our mood and behavior are determined in part by our genes, but always in relationship to our environment also. Our individual good mental health probably depends on how we adjust to ourselves, that is, how we adjust to our own genes and how well we can adjust to our environment. This suggests consideration of the satisfactions that are essential for our good mental health and perhaps the anxieties that continue to drive us to seek them. We are going to turn, then, to Dr. Ralph Gerard, who from his great wisdom and his great scientific ability can give us much on which we will continue to think.

RALPH M. GERARD, M.D.

Since I have no formal presentation ready, I was jotting down things I might say when the ball bounced in my direction. But I am so intrigued by what Sir John—I shall call him Jack, because that's the way I know him better—said that I can't resist starting by taking his outstretched hand.

I remember so well, I think it was just 17 years ago, when he and I were talking about mental activity and I discovered, to my surprise, that he believed in free will. We have been arguing about it on and off in the intervening decade and a half or more, and obviously neither of us will ever convince the other, as I doubt either one of us will convince anyone in the audience, but I thought it might be interesting to go over his eloquent and convincing presentation and see what I can do to counter it.

He started by saying that the way one has to see the world, to place one's self in the universe, was from the inside out, starting with one's own subjective experience. This, of course, is the way it all began. Before the time of the Greeks, you will recall, everyone who thought at all about what was outside themselves, projected themselves out into it. They had the feeling of subjective freedom, the ability to do what they wanted, of being able to be capricious and uncontrolled, so they populated everything they saw with equivalent spirits, which had the freedom that they had. And thus gods multiplied all over the place.

In personal relation to the rest of the universe, when somebody did something you didn't like, you were apt to be hostile and perhaps do something back. When wind blew and upset your canoe or a rock stubbed your toe or a palm frond fell down and smashed your roof, it was because you had somehow offended the spirit of the wind or the rock or the tree. You knew that. Since this was a bigger spirit than you, in many cases, you tried to propitiate the bigger spirit and avoid developing his animosity.

This is what some of the archeologists, particularly Frankfurt, have called the mythopoeic or myth-making mind. It is perhaps one of the greatest contributions of the Greeks, and the first step toward the kind of world that we now live in psychologically as well as physically, that the notion of regularity and cause rather than chaos and caprice came into the world. This, I think, is what the Greeks gave to us—the notion that things do not happen without some potentially understandable basis for them. Then the whole sweep of the Renaissance was toward more and more acceptance of the notion of regularity—that things don't just happen because some incorporeal or incorporated spirit went ahead and made them happen. This notion first developed in the regularity of the movements of the planets. Later the great contributions of Newton and Galileo established the principle of causality. Relatively simple phenomena of nature came to be understood, quantitatively and predictably. People developed a feeling of confidence in the regularity of the world.

Jack said that modern physics is not quite so easily content with the simple notion of direct causality. There is some indeterminism in our concepts; yet, the difference between now and then is in terms of recognizing regularity and predictability in the physical world. First it was limited to the earth; then it went to the heavens. When Bunson, with his 19th century spectroscope, could find the same chemicals in the sun and stars that were known on the earth, this gave tremendous impetus to the idea that the universe is understandable.

Then we began to understand living systems a little. We had to cope with the idea of a vital force, utterly irreconcilable with the material notion of the physical world. After making urea, proteins, and other life chemicals, we learned that there is no special vital force involved in living things. We learned that man is not a different kind of animal from other animals. Now we, our generation in the current decade, are learning that behavior is also predictable and understandable—it is more and more quantified and made simple. I will come back to this in a moment.

To get from the subjective experience out to the world around us, one has to appreciate nonsubjective things and events. One must think of oneself as an entity, an object, rather than a subject, and be able to place one's body, as an object, with the rest of the bodies and entities in the world. Jack did touch upon the effect of experiencing input through one's senses in shaping our picture of the world, and with his account I agree. I would like to elaborate it just a bit.

The more one studies the brain and changes that are induced in it by experience, the more clear it is that the brain itself, as the body at a simpler level, is a product of the environment. I do not dispute the notion of evolution in terms of survival by natural selection. We are products of our environments and our brains are acted upon by our environments to be what they are in detail. There is a great richness of experimentation, in which several in this room have participated, which has demonstrated in more and more detail that the kind of perceptual ability that one has, the kind of motor capacity that one has, the kind of conceptualization that one is able to engender in oneself is largely the result of the kind of experience one has had.

A dramatic experiment was made a couple of decades ago. Baby chimpanzees were kept in the dark from the time of birth to a couple of months of age, and nothing was done to their brain, to their eyes, or to their bodies. They were given good care, a keeper came in and fed them regularly, and this was all they experienced. Nevertheless, not having had the experience of patterned vision during the maturation of the nervous system, when they were later given patterned experience the nervous system couldn't use it. They were functionally blind.

The same situation is found in humans. If one grows up with an opaque or distorted cornea or lens, even though in later life the correction can be made by surgery and one has a perfect cornea, one then does not develop good vision and in many cases never can really use the visual faculties. The brain got past the stage of being manipulated by its environment, past the point of no return.

Now before Dr. Eccles or I or anyone else in the world can even have the notion of "I," in counterdistinction to "you" or "it," there has to be some way of identifying an entity. The whole ability to identify entity is a result of experience. In the development both of the individual child and the social culture, one sees first physical objects of about the same time and space scale as oneself. These are the first things that develop identity or entity or individuality, and it is these which constitute the nouns of the language, the things that we see.

Seeing a thing is by no means a primitive, easy matter; it is a very complex psychological and physiological process and, without going into any more neurophysiology, the whole organization of the retina, and indeed the brain path from the retina, is such as to tremendously accentuate the difference where two different fields of light or color come together. In other words, an edge is greatly exaggerated and distorted. This helps us identify things. The whole history of the emergence of the individual and of society, our whole racial development, has been a progressive recognition of more sophisticated kinds of entities, not merely physical ones, but functional ones, pathological ones, and developmental ones. As we proceed by experience from recognizing a single entity, we first see only an individual at our level, and then realize that it has different kinds of parts within it and also that it is one of a larger group, so that it would be impossible to start in oneself, as one might think one does, without recognizing that all of this comes from the outside. If you weren't there to receive it, you wouldn't get it.

I think the problem is a little bit like an historic episode that I think took place in San Francisco when the transcontinental railway had been completed. There was a great celebration. A train was going to start from Oakland and go east. All the dignitaries of the town were there for the excitement and celebration, and finally the big moment came; the engineer opened the throttle and off went the engine—leaving the train behind. Somebody had forgotten to couple it. I think that it is this coupling problem that is paramount.

Let us come back specifically to the question of predictability and free will. That awareness depends on the central nervous system seems to be agreed upon by all. The more one explores this in detail, the more tight parallelisms one finds. One of the dramatic experiments of a decade or so ago involved burying wires in the depths of the human brain; it was found that whenever a psychotic patient is developing hallucinations certain kinds of electrical activity appear in a certain part of the brain. Well, you say, all right, the hallucination produced the electrical activity. On the other hand, if one gave a sedative drug that could act presumably upon the brain and not on a hallucination, it would stop both the electrical activity and the hallucination. Conversely, if there were no hallucination and this particular part of the brain was stimulated by the indwelling wire, it would start both the electrical activity and the hallucination.

Older experiments are now widely extended. One can bury wires in different parts of the brain and by electrical stimulation evoke almost any kind of experience or emotion or behavior.

Maybe Ken Colby, more an expert in this area than I, would care to expand upon posthypnotic suggestion. There are many experiments in which it is shown that under hypnosis when it has been suggested that the subject will do something at a certain time later, he does it. If he is asked why he does it, he always has a perfectly good reason for choosing to do it, even though the reason sometimes seems far fetched to the listener. But he hasn't really done it through volition. In one sense, then, this was a caused action.

Under strong carbon dioxide inhalation, it has been reported that a subject may will to move an arm—a voluntary action—and nothing happens, and then maybe half a minute later, to his consternation, because the chemical situation in the brain is changed, the action takes place when he is no longer willing it and not even ready to have it happen.

In the world at large, instances of a pseudo "mental telepathy" are not frequent, but they certainly are widespread. Some people develop an uncanny knack of predicting what other people are going to do next or of even knowing what others are thinking—husbands and wives are pretty good at that, and good friends often find conversation is curtailed because after the first word of a new gambit, they know pretty well what the last word is going to be.

These are all examples of predictability of human behavior. I'll give you one other experimental study. Two high school girls who had absolutely no contact with each other were used as subjects. One of them, under hypnosis, was told, "You are asleep, you have just wet your bed, you are having a dream, describe that dream." A recording was made of this description. Then another high school girl was put under hypnosis and was told, "You are asleep, you are having this dream," and then the dream of the other girl was played to her, and she was asked, "What does it mean?" The answer was, "It means I wet my bed." Now the dream was completely in terms of Freudian symbolism and had nothing to do with any easily identifiable picture of such behavior.

I give you these examples, of which one can produce a large number, to show that in spite of our subjective feelings of freedom and volition the more we examine the situation the more we find causal relation. While I do not contend at all that a computer, no matter how intricately we elaborate it so as to be able to parallel the kind of behavior that man is capable of, will thereby generate some kind of subjective experience, I wouldn't deny this as a possibility. What I would deny is that, if it generates some kind of subjective experience, this subjective experience is going to be able to alter the passage of electrical messages from relay to relay and change what comes up. In the same way, I find it impossible to imagine how an idea, whatever that means, can discharge a nerve cell; nor can I imagine the kind of uncaused cause which would be involved in having an idea come without something happening in the nervous system to produce it.

Although Jack is certainly wise in emphasizing our vast ignorance of the nervous system, I am not quite so impressed by the fact that we have studied only a few hundred or a few thousand cells out of ten billion in our brains. While there may be ten billion cells in a human being, there are not ten billion kinds of different cells. We have learned a lot about a number of neurons, and we have learned a lot about the nature of their activity. We are beginning to learn something about the nexus of the patterns in which they operate. Eddington said so well so long ago, "We used to think if we knew one, we knew two, because one and one are two. But we found we must learn a great deal more about 'and.'" It may come out when you have your "and" in there with an "and" of mine that we are in the same universe of discourse.

Now, one last word. Jack is going to come back and say I can't prove what I have said; he'll say that we have to start with awareness, and I will have to agree. The hypothesis of free will is a good hypothesis if you want to use it. I object that it lacks the merit of a good scientific hypothesis. Suppose that we were to hypothesize that mental illness is produced by free will. It would explain everything about mental illness so easily that one could scarcely disprove it, and a hypothesis that one cannot examine in order to disprove it is not useful scientifically.

Finally, on the business of predictable behavior: The other day, at a talk at a luncheon of the National Association of Mental Health, I told the following story and it has popped back into my mind. If you don't think behavior is reasonably predictable, what do you think of the account

of the dear little old lady who called the telephone people and said that
a couple of telephone linemen outside her window had been using vile,
obscene, thoroughly disgusting language in loud voices. The men were called
in and asked what happened. They said, "nothing at all, we were just
doing our job." Asked what they were doing, they said they were busy
brazing a new line across there. When pressed about the lady's complaint,
one of the men finally said, "Well, I think I know what she is referring to.
I was standing down below and Bill was up there with this molten lead
in the ladle and he got a little careless and some of it fell inside my collar
and I may have raised my voice a little. But all I said was, 'Bill, I would
be very grateful if you would be a little more circumspect in the way you
handle that liquid metal.'"

DR. LEAKE: I think we all enjoyed the rather wistful manner in which
Ralph phrased a hope for agreement on that obvious statement that awareness is dependent upon the central nervous system.

I would like to add a point to this historical background with which
Ralph started to explore ancient socializing influences. I remind you that
certain chemicals found in fermented beverages, and other things such as
mushrooms, were used very anciently, and still are, for bringing about individual mental health, perhaps by merging individuals into social survival.
It is also interesting to point out, Ralph, the recent experiments with rats,
showing that when challenged by multiple potential activity, they grow
bigger brains with much more amounts of certain chemicals in those brains
than do unchallenged controls.

Well, we will go on now to a presentation from Professor Colby.

KENNETH MARK COLBY, M.D.

I don't plan to get into an argument about free will with neurophysiologists, but if I were attempting to build an artificial intelligence, I would
give it the feeling that it had free will because I would want the system
to continue to maintain itself. But I guess I should say something about
myself before I say something about what I think are the limitations and
possibilities of people. First, I'm a psychiatrist and psychoanalyst; I spend
a number of hours every day talking to patients—and that is my clinical
experience. Now this talk—this dialogue with patients—involves a very
mysterious sequence of events, it seems to me, as a method for relieving
people of mental distress; these therapeutic conversations (and I define
them as therapeutic by intent) seem to produce changes in people's be-

havior. Their degree of negative effect goes down; behavior patterns change; thought distortion becomes undistorted. In trying to study that kind of person-on-person or individual-on-individual influence, the use of conventional methods is very difficult; no one who has tried conventional methods, such as studying clinical situations, photographing them, tape recording them, doing content analyses of them, gets very far. It ends in head counting, and I think it will take us a hundred thousand years to learn anything that way. Another way is to try to create experimental analogues. That is difficult to do with human beings—not only for ethical reasons. You don't want to fool around with people's beliefs and mental pain in an experimental way for ethical reasons. Methodologically it is just too difficult. You can't separate the independent variables—you don't know what is doing what to what. Because of this, we turn to the possibility of creating an artificial intelligence, that is, creating a model or a system which simulates or imitates a certain type of mental function; if we feel we have created or invented such a system we can then experiment with it and play with it and push variables in different directions hoping to learn something eventually about the real world. So my research interest is in the area of artificial intelligence, computer models, computer simulation of thought and affect. As for artificial intelligence, one commonly stated definition of it is: the attempt to enable a computer to do what people do when we say the latter are behaving intelligently. Notice, I don't use the word "machine." I don't want to get into arguments about machines. I don't think a computer is a machine. It certainly wouldn't be, to Descartes. To Descartes a machine was a bunch of levers and ropes and pulleys, and if he looked at a computer, he wouldn't call that a machine. We thought for a while that all we had to do was ask ourselves the question, "Do machines think?" assuming that we had a clear definition of what a machine was, and the remaining problem was to find out what thinking was. Now I think it is increasingly clear that we don't know what a machine is or even what a computer is. I will say briefly, I don't think a computer is a machine; it is a specialized language. It is a group of symbols tied to our concepts about the world along with rules for operating on those symbols. In a psychiatric clinical situation, it seems to me that one of the limitations of people as individuals is their beliefs. They have certain beliefs about things; they have beliefs about the world; they have conceptions about themselves and in the process of psychotherapy certain of these beliefs are changed, or the therapist tries to change certain of these beliefs—for example, a persecutory paranoid delusion. If a man believes that the FBI is after him, and you have no reason to think they are, you try to modify or change that belief. At a basic science level, we know very little about belief systems. How do belief systems originate, how are they maintained, how are they terminated, and why do they resist change so much? A big problem in people's limitation is their inability to use their minds—their inability to change their minds. How do you change your mind about something? How we *do* change our minds about things is very mysterious. We think if we could find out more about this process, it would increase our abilities to influence mental illness and distress through symbolic input. As you know, there are two methods of dealing with mental illness. One is physical (drugs, shock, surgery, etc.) and the other is through the exchange of semantic information (one person talking to another). A belief system seems very resistent to change. The more a belief involves you and your concept of yourself, the more difficult it is to change it. Now why is that so? Thus far, from our experiments with computer simulations of this kind of belief system, it seems that we don't know enough about input into the system at a certain area of the program—that is, if the information could get into only a particular area of the mind. We have no hesitation in using this old-fashioned, four-letter, Anglo-Saxon word "mind." You can see that the human mind is not just an open sieve or simple tree structure but a nested hierarchy of all kinds of procedures and subroutines. Getting into the right one, getting the input hooked up to the right one, seems to be the big problem. Once you can get it into the right area it will have all kinds of reverberatory effects throughout the system. I think it's much like administering a drug. The point of application is one thing; the point of effect is another. So, I would conclude that we feel one of the big limitations of human individuals consists of their belief systems and inability to change them in ways that might be advantageous. The attempt with computers is to perhaps augment the human intellect or through computer-aided devices to try to help people. If they are not able to change their belief systems, at least they may transcend them in some way through a computer-aided device. The computer is just a tool, an instrument. There are great potentialities in tools and instruments, and we might be able to augment human intellectual function through the use of them.

DR. LEAKE: Very good. I wonder if I might ask you not to leave us hanging here. You indicated belief systems as important from the standpoint of limitations on people as individuals. How about belief systems and their potentialities?

DR. COLBY: To do what?

DR. LEAKE: Live and enjoy life.

DR. COLBY: Oh! I think this: It is from your belief systems, or let's say from "getting them to work the way you feel they should work," that you get your feeling of self-satisfaction or justified self-esteem or whatever it is that keeps people going. By this type of belief system I mean the core beliefs, beliefs about yourself. I don't think that beliefs about whether or not trees are green are really central; it's what you think about yourself that is central. This core belief, this is what runs you. This is where you get your kicks when they are somehow gratified or when you do not develop too many conflicts.

DR. LEAKE: Very good, and now Ralph has something to say.

DR. GERARD: I have a profound example of Ken's point about the difficulty of changing beliefs and the viewpoint that the central ones are the most important. Some of you may not know the story of the man who was convinced he was dead and the psychiatrist tried various devices to change the man's mind, getting nowhere at all. Finally the psychiatrist said, "Well, now would you agree that dead men don't bleed?" "Oh, I agree, of course, dead men don't bleed." "Well, look," and the psychiatrist stabbed the patient with a pin and a drop of blood welled out, and the patient looked at it and said, "I guess I was wrong. Dead men do bleed!"

DR. LEAKE: Well, we can turn now to a consideration of some of the philosophical problems concerning people as individuals to which we have been giving our attention. We will ask Dr. Dennes to let us have the benefit of his wisdom and experience.

WILLIAM R. DENNES, D.PHIL., LL.D.

Well, Dr. Leake, you obviously cannot escape philosophy because you have all been involved in it. In fact, this is a great day for Descartes and for Aristotle. Not only does Sir John say he bases his work on Cartesian principles, but Dr. Gerard was refuting primitive animism by applying the Cartesian principle that an idea cannot act on a body, on a nerve cell. A great day too for Aristotle. Dr. Leake was making very clear the question whether when mental process is biochemically explained we can pretend to have reduced it to biochemical processes or only to have established a correlation between them. And most of us would follow Aristotle and ask Dr. Colby, with respect to the notion that computers are symbol systems and operators, whether sounds can be symbols (or anything else can be symbols) except as they are used with intent to refer to something beyond themselves or to illustrate the syntax which is a relation of a set of symbols. Now I have known a computer when confronted with a contradiction to blush and squeal; but I have never known one to say anything such as "I am alive" or "I am dead," as the psychiatrist's patient insisted he was. But the other day a parakeet confided in me in a very resigned voice: "birds don't talk." I feel reasonably confident that the computer that blushed and squealed was not thinking; but I am not sure that the parakeet had not spotted my trade as logician and philosopher, because all he said to anybody else was "Where's the whiskey?" The bird seemed to be making precisely the point so crucial for Epimenides and Bertrand Russell: If I am a Cretan and say that all Cretans are liars, if I tell the truth I lie; and if I lie, I tell the truth. Exactly the issue raised by the bird who told me birds don't talk.

Well, I really need the help of the computer, because the philosophical issues that all of you gentlemen have raised are so complex that I am moved in about a hundred directions at once. The computer is supposed to be the kind of thing that sorts variables out and puts them in order, isn't it? So I wish Dr. Colby that you had a computer here to do my job for me; but since you haven't, I guess I will get along as well as I can without it. But I can't resist reminding all of you that we have really had in the discussion between Sir John and Dr. Gerard the equivalent of a whole semester's course in the theory of knowledge. Especially challenging was Dr. Gerard's account of the contrast between objects and feelings as the basis for even knowing that one has feelings; and Sir John's contrasting notion that we construct the conception of external objects out of various sense qualities. Now with my passion to reconcile conflicting theories, and to honor the ancient Pythagorean who thought that the function of reason was to make peace, I wonder whether this debate doesn't depend upon our not making up our minds whether what we want to mean by external objects, the external world, is something the like of which we have never been acquainted with, something totally out of our awareness, or whether we make the distinction between inner and outer (this may sound paradoxical) but make it within experience. Do I distinguish external objects from myself, and what I suppose to be other selves, in terms, not of factors I am never acquainted with, but in terms of my acquaintance with extended objects like men and women and chairs, plus the fact that chairs seem to give no indication of remembering, of expecting, of feeling pain, pleasure, remorse, resentment, or whatever, whereas what we call "persons" do. Well, I would hope that the case might be made for the distinction between inner and outer as a distinction with which we are acquainted, and not as a distinction between the whole of what we are acquainted with and something, I know not what, which is totally out of experience.

In the same vein, to say a little about the problem of free will, Sir John is very properly (and much to my admiration) a critic of those who would merely follow fashion. But I wonder if he follows a little too much the fashion of saying that the notion of causation has been discarded and is [interruption by Sir John]. . . .

DR. DENNES: Didn't you say, well maybe I misunderstood you, I thought you said that causation was a 19th Century notion; maybe you meant the one to one—

SIR JOHN: Determinism.

DR. DENNES: What did you say, physical determinism? There is no copyright on the word "determinism" and no copyright on the word "cause," and it is very fashionable nowadays to say that since we cannot determine the position and motion of a fine-scale particle without deflecting it by precisely the magnitude we would like to measure, there are excellent reasons for the conclusion that fine-scale particles change their paths of motion or state of rest without the change being preceded, accompanied, or "caused" by an "impressed force." Not only did my teachers tell me that this simply couldn't happen, but around 1906 the people in the Prussian Academy of Sciences had put down the principle, no such change without an impressed force, as one that didn't need any further looking into because it was absolutely bedrock. In 16 years, the work of Planck, and in another 10 years I suppose the agreement of all the physicists, discarded this "bedrock" causal principle. But I am not sure that we are justified of giving up the idea of causal relation. When you medical men or psychiatrists ask yourselves what is the explanation of some pathologic process, or when a physicist considering statistical relations of immense numbers of fine-scale particles asks for the explanation of spectroscopic shifts, no doubt you are not seeking simple one-to-one correlations of the kind that would have been called in scientifically primitive times cause and effect. Nevertheless, unless we can make out a correlation greater than fifty-fifty, and not just between any factors whatever, but between factors which may have many parameters and rather elastic ones, but in any case are distinguished from just anything you like, I don't think we would regard our statistics as explanatory or enlightening.

I guess Sir John wouldn't differ with me on this; but when we come to determinism and freedom of choice, we need to carry our examination a little farther, because one of the things that worries a great many people is the question whether the proliferation of science, the immense increase of scientific knowledge, isn't showing that we are determined, hedged in on all sides by genetic factors, metabolic factors, factors of conditioning, the influence of economic and other features of the social milieu. The question arises whether our theories and arguments are anything else but reflections of these determining factors; and some are tempted to say that we can only escape that conclusion if we deny determinism and commit ourselves to the notion that will operates freely, independent of causal factors. Do we really want to say that? How can we make sense of saying that acts of choice are *our acts* unless such acts of choice are regularly correlated with our qualities of personality, with our hopes, our fears, our commitments—all of which occur in the world although the study of them is not as yet (I don't think it ever will be) carried out with a precision comparable to that of mechanics. You remember Aristotle's advice that the best test of an educated man was that he looked for precision in the areas in which it was appropriate, and was not so foolish as to look for it where it wasn't appropriate. Some scientists have found correlates of choices in areas that Aristotle would never have dreamed of; but if an act of choice were not as regularly correlated with, as much determined by our personalities, our hopes, our fears, the purposes we entertain, in what sense could we call it our act? In what sense would it be our act if it occurred fortuitously, a bolt from the blue—in what sense could *we* be said to be acting? I am not sure that Dr. Gerard and Sir John are as much at odds on this issue as they think. You see, I feel that on a careful account of moral choice, one would want to find regular correlations between Jones's choices and the habits, hopes, fears, and commitments that make up Jones's personality, since otherwise in what sense would we ever be able to say that a choice was Jones's decision, and not just something that dropped out of the blue. I would, of course, remind you that we hardly think of causation as a relation of enforcement, of enchainment, of necessitation, do we? All we know of it is a degree of regularity of correlation. A friend of mine tells me that there are some cases where it does indeed necessitate: Cutting off a leg doesn't just regularly correlate with one-leggedness; it necessitates it. That throwing a brick with a certain momentum necessitates the window shattering. Well, don't you suppose the man who says cutting off a member reduces the number of members by one would not regard it as a case of cutting off unless the members were thus reduced by one? In other words, if the leg still hangs on by a shred, it is not what he means by an amputation. If it is an amputation then I have one less leg, not because between two distinct transactions there is a necessary connection, but because I mean by the term "amputation" a process that includes the diminution of members; and I suppose by and large the individual who says that the brick moving necessitates the window shattering measures the momentum of bricks by phenomena like shattering windows. Thus, he would say the brick didn't have the momentum that he thought it had if glass of a certain strength didn't shatter when hit by it. Well, I have thought often in the last two days as I have listened to the scientists, sociologists, medical men, psychiatrists, people looking after our schools—I have thought often of Henry Adams' conviction that the increase and proliferation of human knowledge was going on at such a rate that by about 1950 the mind of man would collapse, not only because there would be so much more theory to be understood, but also because the technology that he thought the dynamo was introducing would produce ways of living so complicated that we just wouldn't be equal to them. Well, Dr. Colby can tell us that what Henry Adams knew about, and predicted of, the dynamo has turned out to be a mere drop in the bucket. Whether we have collapsed or not maybe the psychiatrists and psychoanalysts present can tell us, but, at least, we have been acting as if we hadn't collapsed. Whether the growing complications of the world as understood, and the human processes of adaptation to them, have grown in such complexity that we shall fail to manage them, depends a great deal upon the question that my colleagues have been discussing—is it the case that the neurocerebral factors, the metabolic factors, genetic factors, the conditioning of children, the economic and social determinents, the ways in which propaganda causally influence our choice and our behavior—is it the case that these are stripping man of his most human characteristic: deliberate intention, in purpose and choice? As I suggested in a preliminary way a while ago, if we mean by freely chosen actions uncaused actions, fortuitious, capricious, and unaccountable, I should agree with Dr. Gerard. But if we mean by freely chosen actions, actions in which our habits and hopes and fears and purposes and commitments operate, and not just external determinents, then one can always find as much hope as discouragement in the proliferation of knowledge. I suppose that knowledge, as science of the way things are, can never tell us what we ought to prize, what we ought to do, can it? But it can help us enormously in determining the courses of conduct that are likely to nourish the values that we may prize. I should have asked one of these experts, perhaps Dr. Leake, a while ago how much arsenic it takes to kill a man.

DR. LEAKE: Varies with the individual.

DR. DENNES: Tell me a good big dose—40 grains?

DR. LEAKE: Well, yes.

DR. DENNES: Dr. Leake, in addition to all his other achievements, is a pharmacologist, and I have no doubt he could give me a very full explanation of the pharmacological and biochemical principles that justify us in saying that 40 grains of arsenic can kill a man off. Does it follow from that that I ought not to put 40 grains of arsenic in your coffee or in mine?

DR. LEAKE: You see there are always semantic difficulties. Now arsenic is a metal, a heavy gray metal, and that practically won't kill anybody. Your talking about arsenic trioxide; that's different.

DR. DENNES: Well, if I put 40 grains of arsenic trioxide in the coffee Dr. Leake is going to drink, will I have violated any principle of biochemistry, or will I have supplied one more confirmation of one of its hypotheses?

Well, I fall into anecdotage, which is the privilege of age. Some years ago, lecturing at Columbia, I wanted to illustrate a similar point. I was walking along Amsterdam Avenue, and I wanted to know how much arsenic trioxide would be lethal. So passing a pharmacy, I stopped in and asked the pharmacist how much would be lethal, and he looked at me with great suspicion and wouldn't tell me. I am sure he thought I was not going to illustrate a point in the relation between science and values, but rather to commit a murder.

DR. LEAKE: Now there is a belief system here—a belief system. . . .

DR. DENNES: Well, I would suggest that scientific knowledge and moral judgment are not in conflict, but also that science cannot itself establish a judgment of what we ought to do—cannot establish a moral judgment. You see I think that when we would all say, as we all would, that if 40 grains of arsenic trioxide is the lethal dose, of course, you ought not to eat it or give it to your friends, we are relying on another unexpressed premise. We are assuming that we and everybody else prize life above death, health above disease, but without that premise those sheer facts about the usual results of eating arsenic trioxide would not carry any "ought" statements at all, just "is" statements; and can you get an "ought" statement out of an "is"? Can you, out of "what is the case?" determine "what ought to be the case"? You know many years ago when Tolstoy wrote the Kreutzer Sonata and argued that the human race was getting so distracted by carnal feelings, neglecting the arts and sciences and everything worthy of men, that they should give up sexual attachments. Well, there were plenty of people who thought they could refute Tolstoy scientifically by pointing out that if his advice were adopted there soon wouldn't be any people around to cultivate the arts and sciences. Did they refute Tolstoy? No, because if the earth was inhabited by a scum so distracted by carnal feelings he thought it better to eliminate it. In other words, not the existence of life itself conveys any absolute imperative but the love, the approval, and indeed the quality of the life lived. In the past two days no one has argued that living a thousand years would as such be better than living a hundred or eighty or sixty years. Really we have all been saying what Immanual Kant and David Hume insisted on: Namely, that moral judgments are autonomous—you cannot produce them, control them by knowledge of matter of fact—not even by knowledge of the structure of the universe. If you have a comprehensive metaphysic incorporating the best confirmed scientific hypotheses, there may be no better instrument to guide you to achieve the purposes you cherish. If you asked what ought to be the content of moral attitudes— what this extra premise, besides knowledge of matter of fact, ought to be (maybe none of you feel we should ask ourselves that question; perhaps you feel the answer is too obvious)—well, if you ask me, I would begin with a pretty obvious kind of answer. Whether from Plato, or from the scriptures of three great religions that I am acquainted with, or from the writings of Kant—namely the Golden Rule—to make only such choices as for others under these circumstances or myself at another time, I would equally approve. And if you tell me that rule is empty—that it says to do right, but what is right?—well, I would rely greatly on what people were saying here the last two days and upon what little I have been able to learn from other physiologists, psychologists, and anthropologists about needs basic to creatures like us. We may call certain needs basic, not just in the sense of being widespread (although they do manifest themselves, my anthropologist friends assure me, in all the human groups with which they are acquainted —those that we conceitedly call lower, as well as those we compare with ourselves) but also in the sense that if blocked they derange or terminate the functioning of the organism. Many of you who are students of these things are probably more aware than I am that needs for affiliation, the curiosity drive, the impulses that manifest themselves in play and in artistic expression and enjoyment, succorance needs, nurturance needs are quite as basic to human beings as are needs for food, drink, sex, excretion, and so on. The satisfaction of these inevitably involves conflict, and yesterday we had two very beautiful accounts of some of the phases distinguishable in the development of a person from the kinds of conflicts that pretty regularly occur. Well, if we do prefer life to death, and health to disease, is there a way to establish scientifically that life and health* are good? Does our answer to Tolstoy finally express love rather than knowledge, no matter how knowledgeable we may be? If you get the feeling that this "sorry

---

*We should ask those who talked yesterday about health in terms of effective functioning in the satisfaction of all our needs, as against freedom from infection, to spell out in much more detail what they thus meant by "health."

frame of things" is such that you would like just to call it a day and make this a requiem and not a colloquium, what is the answer? I remember at Los Alamos during the war one gifted but very tired scientist arguing that, since we are surrounded by immense quantities of nitrogen, there was an appreciable probability that the minute volume of unstable nitrogen in the laboratory, if released, might start a chain reaction in the atmosphere which would in a few seconds transform our globe into an incandescent sphere, and be the end of all of us. Well, he said, he didn't care if it did. Some said this exhibited the strength of his devotion to science—the duty to explore at all costs, even if it led to the end of everything. I think the chances of a nitrogen holocaust were too remote to be worth thinking about; but was there any way theoretically to refute his moral judgment? No matter how much we tell him of the scientifically probable consequences of a course of action, unless at some stage he prefers life to death and health to disease, there is no earthly way of establishing by scientific or metaphysical knowledge that Tolstoy's advice should not be taken or that the scientists should not take his chances, and the world's chances, by releasing the unstable nitrogen.

The ancient values not just of truth, beauty, and goodness, but also of health, knowledge, and love: what is the justification of these? One can carry out a very complicated preliminary to their justification in terms of the satisfaction of needs basal to creatures like us. But when all that is done, one is up against St. Paul's advice that knowledge and power are worthless without love. Thus, finally, the basis of moral judgment will be found to be, not knowledge of the way things are, but love: genuine preference for life over death and for health over disease. Many protest: "That is so obvious. Why does one waste even three or four minutes in saying it?" Well, it may be obvious that without this usually suppressed premise judgments of fact can never yield judgments of value. But it is not obvious at all, although we may all do lip service to it, that the impoverishment and destruction of life, if out of sight, and not our lives or our friends, and not by violently killing people off, but by reducing their activity and effectiveness (which is a slow kind of dying)—if all this is out of sight, it is not at all obvious that we are genuinely and honestly committed to preferring health to disease and life to death.

The more the scientists can tell us (and they have been telling us an awful lot this afternoon and during the last two days), and with computers to rely on to keep things in order if they get too complicated, the better position we shall be in to make choices: choices that are effective because they are made in the light of knowledge of regular correlations which is all that one can mean, I think, by causation, although we tend carelessly to try to mean enforcement by the notion. If the game doesn't get so complicated that we can't understand it, we have a better chance of playing it effectively than ever before.

Whether I have done anything to bring my colleagues together, or have only irritated them, we shall soon see.

DR. LEAKE: Thank you, Dr. Dennes. I am going to take the liberty of making a comment of my own, and then I am going to ask Dr. Colby to answer a question that was submitted to him by Dr. Friedgood. Later we hope Sir John will take up the commentary, and then perhaps open whatever free discussion we might wage. Those of the audience who wish to send notes for comment, please do so now.

My comment is this: That in spite of what I said in introducing the colloquium this afternoon, regarding the dangers of extrapolating from one level of biological organization to another, I fear that we have made an extraordinary jump from the behavior of nuclear particles to the motivation of human individuals in the matter of free will. Quite as Aristotle pointed out a propriety with respect to precision, there is also a propriety with regard to semantics—certain words have meaning in certain contexts, but we must be sure to keep those contexts in order. Determinism in regard to minute nuclear particles is quite a different thing from determinism in regard to human behavior.

Now Dr. Colby would you please reply to Dr. Friedgood's question?

DR. COLBY: The question is: Does not the concept of psychotherapy as exchange of semantic information, which is what was said, ignore the factor of a meaningful subjective relationship existing between therapist and patient?

My answer to that question is "No." The exchange involves the interrelationship. Effective psychotherapy depends on the sharing and exchange of mutually meaningful information, based on the subjective interrelation between therapist and patient. One of the big problems in all behavioral science is how to extract meaning—that is, semantics, from natural language. Semantic exchange would include the subjective relationship between therapist and patient.

DR. LEAKE: This matter of meaningful relationships is important for mental health. But now, Sir John, go ahead.

SIR JOHN: Not all of this, you know, is the full picture. We do agree on a great many matters. Ralph told us that, because primitive man was so sure of his own consciously experienced feelings, he erroneously projected them to inanimate nature. All movements were supposed to result from some spirit, some animistic idea inhabiting material objects.

Now, I never have seen the logic of the argument that because this statement of putting spirits into all inanimate objects were erroneous, therefore the original basis was invalidated, mainly that one fears a cause within oneself. It's rather like going at the baby with the bath water. Admittedly early man was wrong; we always try making inferences, but often the basis on which we make them is incorrect or we are guilty of some illogical process in our thinking.

We must be certain that people have not had a spiritual cause within themselves. I only ask you to remember that this spiritual inner feeling is something that is a direct experience of ours. I agree, however, that the predictability of human behavior depends on the extent of our understanding of people and on our knowledge of their makeup and their environment. So, in spite of our subjective feeling of freedom of volition, we are given to understand that our actions have a causal basis, so that they are broadly determined and we could understand them if we only knew all that went into the inheritance and the conditioning of any particular individual, including ourselves. I'll come back to this.

We were told by Dr. Gerard that it is utterly impossible to imagine how an idea can discharge a nerve cell. Of course, I find it impossible to imagine this too. We have such an ignorance of the mode of action of the brain that I would not even know how to start to do an investigation. But I would not deny the possibility. I would only say I don't know about it. No one can make such a statement and base it upon scientific evidence.

It's not the individual nerve cell that is the problem. The problem is the brain and the organized complexity of a network involving ten thousand million neurons, each of them linking to millions within a second of time and each one firing in sequence. It isn't a matter of there being ten thousand million patterns possible in the brain; it is ever so much greater than these incalculable complexities.

We don't know even the most simple pattern involved in the most simple perception. Nor do I know when we will be able to deliver the information about such a pattern. All we can do is pick out one nerve cell or another nerve cell that is one unit in a pattern involving millions of nerve cells, and this tells us little of what takes place in the brain as a whole. Even the simplest experience must involve a pattern spreading in space and time to millions of neurons.

Ralph said that free will lacks the merit of a good scientific hypothesis because there is no way in which it can be disproved. I didn't put it forward as a scientific hypothesis; I put it forth merely as a metaphysical hypothesis.

Your hypothesis is also a metaphysical hypothesis. By the same token, I ask you, can you define the experimental investigation that would disprove your hypothesis that all behavior is determined and conditioned? I am sure you must say, "No"—you can't define it. Thus your hypothesis is just as metaphysical as mine.

DR. GERARD: I'll have to think about that one. I don't think so.

This makes me think of a favorite gambit that a professor of geology used to use in opening an introductory course in science at the University of Chicago. He came into the room with all the freshmen in front of him and waited until everyone was quiet. Then he said, "I was created last night; you were created last night; the whole world was created last night; the libraries and the books in them were created last night; we were created with memories of the past; there were fossils created in the rocks last night; I challenge anyone in this room to disprove me."

SIR JOHN: Two more things if you can bear it. I want to take issue with Dr. Dennes about a matter. One can try out whether willing leads to action, not in major moral decisions, perhaps, but in the most trivial and capricious acts, such as tearing a piece of paper. Should I tear it or not? I think that's the test; if, in the most trivial and capricious things, we can do what we please, and we can change as often as we like, and in any manner that we please, regardless of background or surroundings, then we show freedom of will. Consider cases of compulsion neurosis where people suffer from a disability to act with such freedom.

One may say that I am merely conditioned to tear up pieces of paper on occasion, given an appropriate trigger stimulus. One may say I didn't know that I was conditioned to do that, but that it is known—well, I'm just saying you are asking me to believe something which is completely beyond my capacity to believe.

DR. GERARD: If I told you to do that under hypnosis and you did it, and then I asked you why you did it, what would you say?

SIR JOHN: My answer would be the same, and I wasn't being hypnotized by you when I would say it.

DR. LEAKE: Let's not go too far in this hypnotic performance. We have some questions. I ask Dr. Colby, please, if he will answer a couple of questions that are addressed to him.

DR. COLBY: One question relates to experience in psychotherapy showing that people do change their beliefs. "Could the principles that have been discovered in psychotherapy be used in education? Could these principles improve ways of communication in education?"

I would say that could be so. The trouble with us in psychiatry is that we don't know what we have learned exactly—that is, in the psycho-therapeutic situation one uses a shotgun prescription, so that thousands of semantic interchanges take place between therapist and patient. We don't know which are necessary or sufficient for a change in belief to occur. Until we have a greater knowledge of what can be left out and what really is at the heart of person-on-person influence, I don't think we have any sound principles to introduce into education.

Speaking of belief systems, those of us on the panel have revealed some of our belief systems. I think we don't know enough to influence one another when it comes to these kinds of beliefs. Someone might raise the question that we will never know anyway. Maybe we should not try to reconcile individual differences but promote them, or even create them, since out of conflict comes novelty and variety, and if we all are having a general consensus then we are probably merely deceiving ourselves.

DR. LEAKE: Here is a question for Dr. Dennes. Would you say that we could agree that health means preferring life to death?

DR. DENNES: Saying that health is good expresses a preference for life over death. Health implies a joyousness in life, but does not necessitate a preference for life over death. Good mental health may involve recognition of the inevitability of death, and of preparing to meet it with dignity.

DR. LEAKE: This answer, then makes the next question a little unnecessary. This question indicates one of the belief patterns that we tend to have, thanks to Freud. The question is: "Does not a notion, then, that health is good indicate the strength of the will or wish to die?" And I think that you would agree with me that the answer to that is a tentative "no."

DR. DENNES: Well, unless you take things by opposites.

DR. LEAKE: Our attitudes toward living, toward health, toward dying have much to do with the way in which we behave. Our beliefs do fashion our behavior. A question?

AUDIENCE: I am wondering if some psychoanalyst in the audience would comment on the Freudian concept—the psychoanalytic concept—and relate it to belief systems that somehow seem immutable and unchangeable.

DR. LEAKE: This is Dr. Colby's field. Do you want to comment?

DR. COLBY: I think if you start studying a given individual's belief system, you can arrange it into a type of hierarchy—or in concentric circles if you want to think visually of a central core of beliefs, certain of which are very difficult to change, for example "My name is ——————." Now, as you know from all kinds of experiments, it is very difficult to change that belief. The range is from such a firm belief to extremely peripheral beliefs which are very easily changed; for example, I think political beliefs are very often easily changed in some people, or beliefs about things that don't make much immediate difference—e.g., life on Mars. I could change your belief on this easily, I think.

Maybe I should clarify what I mean by a belief, because this is the unit I am talking about. Belief is any proposition held as true. It is a proposition, a mental state, a state of affairs held as true. In other words, it has a certain probability value on it. A personal subjective probability value. Psychoanalysts are in the business of changing degrees of beliefs, particularly those beliefs that are involved in severe neurotic conflicts. We have found from around sixty years of experiences that some beliefs can be changed easily; others are extremely difficult if not impossible to change with the state of knowledge that we now have.

DR. LEAKE: Regarding the rigidity of association patterns, let me ask you this: "From a semantic point, how would you differentiate belief from faith?"

DR. COLBY: I would say faith is a type of belief.

DR. GERARD: May I get in this for a moment? The discussion comes back to the talk I didn't give. The essence of individuality, I think, is that the more complicated the living system, the more its present state depends on its particular past—that is, its own individual past. A given atom doesn't differ much from another atom of the same kind because there are very few ways in which atoms can be changed by what happens, and its changes are often reversible. On the other hand, a complex protein molecule is very much influenced by its own past experience. It may be denatured by a rather trivial experience and have difficulty in ever getting back to the way it was before. If such is possible at a macromolecular level, it is vastly more possible at a cellular level or with a total individual with billions of neurons. The phenomenon is even more noticeable at the level of large groups of individuals in societies, which in themselves are kinds of large-scale organisms. But the point is that the more complex the system, the more it depends on what has happened to it and therefore the more chance you have for variation and individuality, and specificity in what it will do in its choice of value systems and everything else.

My own view is that in comparing neurotic vs. psychotic states, the neurotic state, which is a certain kind of unacceptable or variant behavior, is brought about by the sort of experience that the individual has had. This experience has been of predominant influence in bringing about the particular kind of neuron connection and pattern and functioning hierarchy which exists in that particular brain. Just as learning produces changes in the brain as a result of experience, so the particular experiences that that person has had, have led to a particular kind of behavior. The more profound, the more repeated, the earlier in life that particular experience led to the molding of the brain in that kind of patterned structure, the harder it is going to be to alter it. This is why psychotherapy of neurosis cannot be a one-shot, easy, universal job.

It is the great merit of psychotherapy that, by putting in a new pattern of experience, repeating it, developing it, there is the chance of building up a new kind of pattern structure of the functioning neurons of the brain which will ultimately lead to a new kind of behavior and a new kind of belief and value system. But, as Colby said—and I agree with him—the older, the more basic to one's personality these things are, the harder it is to alter them. Indeed the very deep ones are probably not possible to change, just as few of us could learn a new foreign language at our age, and learn to speak it without an accent. We are too firmly fixed.

DR. LEAKE: Would you care to comment, Dr. Colby?

DR. COLBY: Is learning, then, a process of association, or can William Stern's theory of learning by the individual child as a process of disassociation be applied to the larger topic under discussion? All learning theories of the moment are too simple because they don't come to grips with three central things about human experience: (1) That people think; (2) that they talk; and (3) that they have self-awareness.

I would like to make a point about Sir John's remark about awareness in machines, awareness in computers. We are going to be driven into the wall sooner or later. Logically perhaps, after a tribute to machines, we may be willing to say that a computer has some self-awareness, if we are going to use the same logical methods that we use now when we say I have awareness, and when I am willing to say that you have awareness because you tell me about it, and behave like I do in certain circumstances, and when I find your testimony in other situations reliable. I would see no objection to admitting that some very complicated electrical chemical system such as computers of the future could have awareness and could have some "feeling."

DR. LEAKE: This is a broad statement, and it brings up a lot for future discussion. We should close by asking each member of the panel if there is anything further that might be said. I would like to take advantage of my own position to summarize a little. Would any of you care to make any comment?

DR ECCLES: To go back to this computer idea of self-awareness, I think that it is an amusing hypothesis, but why bother with it.

DR. LEAKE: If we are to consider awareness in a computer, we do have to keep ourselves aware of the semantic significance of what we say. Terms that have been developed over the ordinary course of human experience may cloud us a bit when we are getting into technologies that are new and strange and taking us into paths that we haven't dreamed of. We may have to learn a new technical language, or derive words or symbols that will keep us aware of the conditions under which we are speaking. Ralph, do you have a comment?

DR. GERARD: I can't resist a final story—aside from pointing out that when Sir John was speaking and I hadn't hypnotized him, he was probably hypnotizing himself. Our argument is really a never-ending one. Perhaps we are in somewhat the situation of the evangelist speaker who was extolling the nature of the world and heaven, and stated that the earth is supported on a great rock. Someone in the audience said, "Yes, but what holds up the rock?" The preacher said, "Another rock," and then glared at the man, subsided, and finished his sermon. But the question kept nagging him, and when he finished, he looked back at the questioner and said, "It is rock all the way down."

DR. LEAKE: Like our discussion, it is solid.

We have one last question: "Would it not be good for some of these problems to be discussed in high school; would it not help young people to find relaxed adaptation to modern pressures?"

I don't know whether it would or not. And I am not sure to the extent to which these kinds of discussions which we are holding at this level are appropriate for high school students. High school students may have neither the interest, nor the background for our sort of discussion, but we might make a trial.

CHAUNCEY D. LEAKE, M.D.

We had a discussion this morning regarding the significance of mental health at various age levels. In connection with it, Mrs. Mahler indicated the significance of anxiety. It is on the relation of anxiety to mental health that I wish to close.

Anxiety may be considered in one way to be the antithesis of satisfaction. It seems to me that we are reaching, from the plethora of our experiences, some agreement in comparing our reactions one with another, as to what we mean by satisfaction. We are also obtaining some insight into the feeling of satisfaction as a result of a more scientific approach relating to chemical events that may take place in certain parts of our central nervous systems that are below the cortex.

I am referring to some of the studies that have been reported by Paul MacLean and others on the hypothalamus and the limbic system in our primitive brain stems. In this jumble of neurons, lie a group of cells that seem, from the very beginning, to direct us physiologically toward self-preservation in the cyclic search for food. This activity may be regulated by a sort of glucostat. When blood sugar goes down to a critical point, the food intake cells described by Brobeck and Anand get active, and we begin our cyclic search for food. When food is ingested and the blood sugar goes up, the food-intake cells shut off, and we have a comfortable feeling of well-being. We are satisfied. There is a conditioning association with our first experience with food intake from our mother's breasts—the warmth associated with the experience, the feeling of comfort—this is satisfaction, and we want it.

Later on, as the metamorphosis of puberty occurs, another group of cells begin a slower cyclic activity. These are associated with the preservation of the species, and regulate the drive for sex. These cells may have a different type of triggering. Their cycle is certainly more prolonged than in the case for food and satisfaction. The activity of these cells regulating the sex drive may be associated with a metabolic buildup of certain types of chemicals, chiefly amines, which are polarized and charged, producing increasing tension to activate the whole individual to achieve orgasm. This apparently occurs when these cells "discharge," as the amines are released, and the cells depolarize and become quiescent, leaving the individual in a relaxed, reposed, satisfied condition.

This sense of satisfaction, of comfort, of well-being, becomes conditioned by varying experiences, but we all want it. As we go along life we may find various ways by which we obtain satisfaction and we are happy when we are satisfied. But inevitably with all of us, at some time or other, there is a suspicion that there is a possibility that we may not be satisfied. This is the feeling of anxiety.

In a certain sense, it is wise for us to have a bit of anxiety if we are to move forward at all. We have to have some drive for living. Some degree of anxiety, therefore, may be useful, helpful in a general overall survival manner. If anxiety persists, however, then a certain psychodynamism results which I think is worth exploring.

If the anxiety goes on a little beyond the point of the possibility that one may not get the satisfactions one seeks in living, the trouble-making psychodynamism begins. When one realizes that there is a probability that one may not achieve satisfaction, then there is frustration. Immediately a peculiar characteristic occurs; we focus our frustration usually on an individual literally and figuratively close to us—parent, sibling, boss, associate, colleague, physician, banker. Thus the frustration goes into resentment. If we don't stop here, the psychodynamism may become acute; we may go from resentment to anger. If we explode angrily, usually it is all over and we come back to equilibrium; and we can start all over again. But if it doesn't, then we may go to rage. Rage, I'll remind you, is uncontrollable—the inside control is gone.

The psychic anxiety can be chronic also. A chronic frustration leading to a chronic resentment, focused again, may go into jealousy. The psychodynamism then may go into envy, or hatred, or vengeance. The end result may be the same disaster, either for the individual or the society in which that individual may be.

It seems to me that an understanding of the potential character of anxiety in relation to satisfaction is something that would contribute to our mental health. If we can keep our anxieties to the point where we do not expect too much, and learn to be satisfied with whatever we do get, maybe we can approach a satisfying or satisfactory condition in mental health.

There is another aspect of this that I think is of extreme importance. It is related to the discussion of Dr. Dennes on moral values, moral judgments, and how science may enter into this matter, if at all. You remember that it was asked by Dr. Dennes how can we get an "ought" from what "is?" It is part of the business of science to tell us what "is." Maybe it can aid in telling us what we ought to do, *if* we want to accomplish something specifically.

We explored this problem out here in the redwoods one time about 25 years ago. With us were E. G. Conklin, then President of the American Association for the Advancement of Science, one of my own teachers, and a great biologist, Olaf Larsell, one of the best neurophysiologists and neuroanatomists, and Judson Herrick of Chicago, one of the keenest of American neurologists. We tried to formulate a scientifically phrased, verifiably descriptive statement that would have moral significance and which would constitute a naturally operative principle—operative whether or not we are aware of it, or like it. This we induced from the plethora of human experience. The principle is that "The probability of survival of a relationship between individuals or between groups of individuals increases to the extent to which that relationship is mutually satisfying." That statement doesn't say anything directly about what we ought to do. It does imply, however, that *if* an individual, who is part of a relationship, wishes that relationship to continue, then it is immediately incumbent upon that individual to make the relationship as satisfying to the others who are in the relationship as to that individual. It is *mutual* satisfaction that is the key to social well-being. The descriptive statement of the conditions for mutual satisfaction implies the normative statement of the Golden Rule or of the Kantian imperative.

INDEX